STARS

A JOURNEY THROUGH
STELLAR BIRTH, LIFE
AND DEATH

STARS

A JOURNEY THROUGH STELLAR BIRTH, LIFE AND DEATH

Raman Prinja
Professor of Astrophysics,
University College London

NEW
HOLLAND

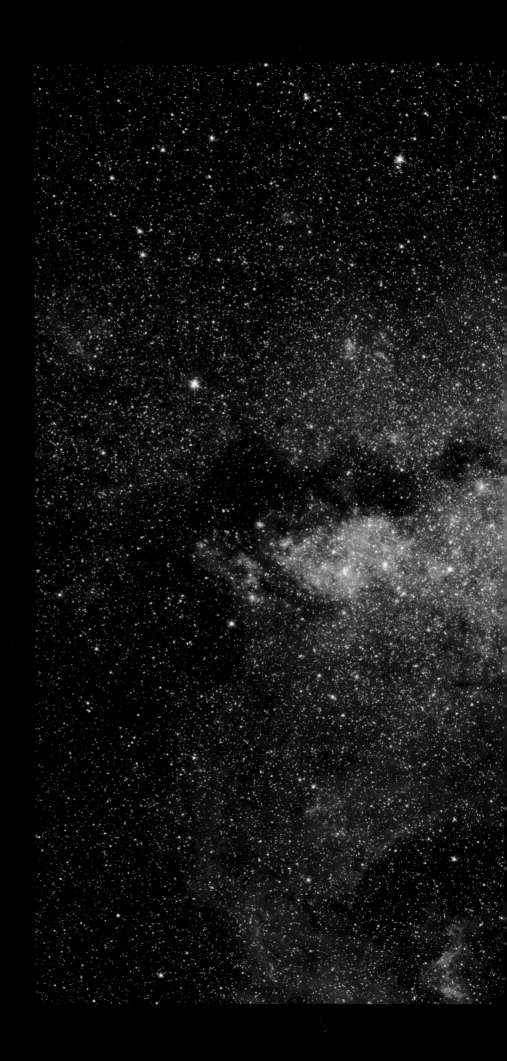

In loving dedication to
Kamini, Vikas and Sachin

Published in 2008 by New Holland Publishers (UK) Ltd
London • Cape Town • Sydney • Auckland

Garfield House, 86–88 Edgware Road,
London W2 2EA, United Kingdom
www.newhollandpublishers.com

80 McKenzie Street, Cape Town 8001, South Africa

Unit 1, 66 Gibbes Street, Chatswood, NSW 2067,
Australia

218 Lake Road, Northcote, Auckland, New Zealand

10 9 8 7 6 5 4 3 2 1

ISBN 978 1 84773 063 3

Publishing Director: Rosemary Wilkinson
Editors: Giselle Osbourne; Steffanie Brown; Julia Shone
Design and Cover design: Neal Cobourne
Production: Melanie Dowland

Front cover image: © NASA, ESA, and the Hubble Heritage
Team (STScI/AURA)-ESA/Hubble Collaboration
Acknowledgment: B. Whitmore (Space Telescope Science
Institute)

Reproduction by Pica Digital PTE. Ltd., Singapore
Printed and bound in Singapore by Tien Wah Press

Contents

Introducing the Stars

LEFT: *A tremendous and fascinating variety of stars is on view in our Milky Way Galaxy.*

One of the most wondrous sights of nature is the star-filled sky viewed far from city lights on a dark, clear and Moon-less night. In these ideal conditions the dark-adapted human eye can pick out almost 3,000 individual stars. This breathtaking global experience has been appreciated by mankind since prehistoric times and ever since, we have sought to understand the patterns, movements and variety of the stars. This book is motivated by the fact that the night sky offers us our most straightforward and direct view of the Universe. Anyone can step outside and gaze up to ponder over fundamental questions about our place in the Universe. The study of stars was one of the first truly scientific pursuits and we strive today to understand their detailed nature, composition and origin. In modern science our knowledge of the stars is essential for studying the Universe and appreciating our own existence. Almost every chemical element in the Universe, aside from hydrogen and helium, is only formed in the intensely hot interiors of stars. The stars are also the primary source of information about galaxies and almost every area of astronomy uses the results from our understanding of how stars live and die.

One of the main discoveries of modern science is that stars are not eternal. The fascinating life-stories of stars are the main subject of this book, which is revealed here using the most detailed and spectacular imagery. Powerful observing facilities such as the Hubble and Spitzer Space Telescopes, together with giant ground-based observatories like the European Southern Observatory in Chile, are today allowing astronomers to probe in great detail the manner in which stars are born, how they change during their lives, and the final stages of their demise. The evolution of individual stars occurs over millions and billions of years and this book presents snap-shots that span from the beauty of giant star making clouds to sparkling clusters of young stars and close-up views of our Sun. We also witness here the death of stars as they go through unstable stages and violent supernova detonations, to ultimately leave behind very exotic stellar tombstones such as black holes. This book is dedicated to providing a widely accessible account of these remarkable phenomena.

LEFT: *A tremendous and fascinating variety of stars is on view in our Milky Way Galaxy.*

LEFT: *A gorgeous view of the night sky seen from the site of the Cerro–Tololo Inter-American Observatory in Chile.*

RIGHT: *The grand Andromeda Galaxy has a similar spiral appearance to our Galaxy.*

A Galaxy of Stars and a Universe of Galaxies

The stars we see in the night sky are a minute fraction of the 200 billion stars that make up our Galaxy, known as the Milky Way Galaxy. Galaxies are vast collections of stars, gas and dust held together by their self-gravity. They are magnificent islands in space that come in a rich variety of shapes and sizes. Our own Galaxy has a flattened, spiral structure, with swirling arms extending out from a dense central bulge of stars and gas. Aside from spiral-shaped galaxies, there are vast elliptical or egg-shaped galaxies, while others are highly irregular with no obvious symmetry.

Our Sun is a rather average star in the Milky Way Galaxy, with a mediocre location just over halfway from the centre to the edge of the disk of the galaxy. At this position, the solar system takes almost 200 million years to complete one orbit around the Galaxy's centre, travelling at a speed of 220 kilometres per second (140 miles per second). Galaxies are rarely found in isolation and most are

surrounded by a swarm of neighbouring galaxies that are locked together by their gravitational influences. Our Milky Way Galaxy is part of a Local Group of 3 large and more than 30 smaller galaxies. The largest member of this group is the stunning Andromeda Galaxy, which, in ideal observing conditions, is the most distant object visible with naked eyes. In the past, some of the dwarf galaxies in the Local Group have even had close encounters or glancing blows with our Galaxy. Indeed collisions and mergers of galaxies are fairly common in tightly packed clusters throughout the Universe. Two of the more conspicuous neighbouring galaxies to ours are the irregular shaped Large and Small Magellanic Clouds, both of which harbour tremendous nurseries for the birth of numerous new stars. Using powerful telescopes astronomers are able to pick out bright individual stars or clusters of stars in other distant galaxies, thus opening up the possibilities for studying the origin and lives of stars in environments that may be very different from those found in our Galaxy.

On a much larger scale, groups of galaxies with a few dozen constituents can be linked together to form even grander structures known as superclusters. The Milky Way Galaxy and the rest of the Local Group galaxies are, for example, part of the Virgo supercluster, which contains thousands of galaxies and a total mass equivalent to a thousand trillion Suns. However despite all this matter, so vast is space that a large volume of the Virgo supercluster is essentially empty of galaxies and stars. The modern picture of superclusters of galaxies arranged in vast walls and sheets, and surrounded by voids of space, represents our modern picture of the Universe on the grandest scales. As we embark here on our journey to explore the stars, it is remarkable to imagine just how many stars there must be in the Universe. With possibly up to a thousand billion galaxies, each loaded with millions or billions of stars, counting up all the stars would be as impossible as trying to count all the dry sand grains on every beach on Earth.

RIGHT: *Hubble Space Telescope image of a diverse cluster of galaxies located over 450 million light-years away.*

A Sense of Scale

Space is very big indeed and the study of stars and galaxies immediately involves distances, sizes and ages that are extreme and not obvious in comparison to our everyday experiences. The distance from the Earth to the Sun of 150 million kilometres (93 million miles) is already hard to appreciate, but that is just a very 'local' distance on stellar scales. The distance from the Earth to the next nearest star beyond the Sun is almost 40 million million kilometres and it is about 250,000 million million kilometres to the centre of our Galaxy. To help visualise these dimensions imagine a scale model where the Sun is represented by a basketball. The Earth would then be a pea placed about 32 metres (105 feet) from the ball and the next nearest star would be another basketball almost 9,000 kilometres (5,600 miles) away. We'd have to fit in another 200 billion basket balls at considerably greater distances just to make a model of our own Milky Way Galaxy.

To avoid awkward large numbers astronomers have devised other units as a measure of the vast distances in space. To discuss the spacing of stars it is appropriate to use a unit of length known as the light-year. One light-year is the distance covered by light in one year, travelling uninterrupted in empty space at a speed of 300,000 kilometres per second (186,400 miles per second). This distance in more terrestrial units would be written as 9,460,000,000,000 kilometres. Light-years are thus units of distance, not time. So for example the distance to the nearest star to the Sun, called Proxima Centauri, is 4.2 light-years and the centre of our Galaxy is about 26,000 light-years away. The dimensions of space are so incredible, however, that in stepping out toward other galaxies we soon start to peer across distances of millions or billions of light-years.

These great distances mean that even light takes a substantial amount of time to reach us from distant stars and galaxies. For instance light takes 8 minutes to reach us from the Sun and almost 43 minutes to travel from the outer planet Jupiter. It takes 9 years for light to cover the distance from Sirius, the brightest star in the night sky, and almost 1,500 years to reach Earth from the bright stars in the prominent constellation of Orion. Light travelling through space is therefore a cosmic time machine. The Andromeda Galaxy is almost 2.5 million light-years away from us, so when we view it through our telescopes we are receiving light that travelled through space for 2.5 million years and we are in effect seeing what Andromeda looked like 2.5 million years ago. The farther an object is in distance, the further back we look in time. The most powerful telescopes of today are capable of detecting galaxies that are more than 12 billion light-years away, which means that we are seeing them as the first substantial collections of stars that were assembled in the infant Universe.

A scale of time in the Universe can be equally difficult to appreciate. The origins of our Galaxy and solar system date back to billions of years, and the life stories of stars unfold over similarly enormous spans of time. The very widely accepted view is that the Universe began with a Big Bang origin that places a maximum age limit of about 13.7 billion years. Let us then mark out major landmarks in the history of the Universe since this time by considering a scale model that compresses 13.7 billion years into just one of our calendar years. In this 'cosmic calendar' the Big Bang occurs at the stroke of midnight on 31 December. Each subsequent month in our imaginary scale then represents more than 1 billion years in the real Universe. Fifteen minutes after midnight all the hydrogen in the Universe was formed. By mid-March a vast cloud of gas had collapsed under gravity to make billions of stars and form our Milky Way Galaxy. Our solar system was assembled by early September and by late September primitive life was flourishing on Earth. Complex life-forms and animals in oceans appeared somewhat later by around mid-December. Though in real time the extinction of the dinosaurs occurred 65 million years ago, in our cosmic calendar this catastrophe would have happened early on 27 December. It is not until close to the end of the year, at 10 p.m. on 31 December that the first hominids appeared on our planet. More humbling is that the entire period of human history from the ancient Egyptians to the 21st century is represented by the final 10 seconds of this scaled year. The period over which mankind has considered the stars in the sky is profoundly insignificant compared to the time span of the Universe itself.

Our understanding of stars and galaxies relies fundamentally on the ability to collect and analyse the faint light that reaches us from distant parts of our Galaxy and beyond. Through advances in technology, computing power and the manufacturing of new materials, astronomers have gained access over the past decade to the most sophisticated observatories ever built. These facilities are providing better defined, highly detailed images than was ever possible before. The latest telescopes are fitted with an array of sensitive light detectors and computer technology. These instruments, which include charge-couple devices (CCDs), spectrographs and segmented mirrors, have transformed astronomical observatories into astrophysical laboratories and opened up a new era of quantitative astronomy and astrophysics.

Modern astrophysics involves the study of radiation from stars and galaxies across a wide range of the electromagnetic spectrum, not just the narrow optical wave band that is visible to our eyes. Hotter and more energetic objects in the Universe release higher energy radiation than cooler objects. To understand the properties of very hot stars or hot gases in the Universe it is necessary to 'tune' the telescopes to the X-ray, ultraviolet and gamma-ray wave-bands. Similarly to study cold matter such as star-making clouds of gas, or to peer through obscuring layers of icy dust in space, astronomers use infrared and radio telescopes. Electromagnetic radiation can be thought of as a stream of mass-less photons travelling through space in a wave-like manner, at the speed of light. The photons contain a certain bundle of energy, which is lower in the case or radio waves, slightly more in infrared, and increasingly more energetic from visible to ultraviolet and X-rays to gamma-rays.

Thankfully for us on Earth, the atmosphere acts like a shield to prevent harmful X-rays and ultraviolet rays reaching the ground. Some of the cosmic infrared radiation is also trapped in the atmosphere. To collect radiation at these wave-bands it is therefore necessary to place the telescopes and detectors in an orbiting satellite well above the Earth's atmosphere. Launching telescopes in space also offers advantages in the visible wave-band, since moving pockets of air act like lenses to distort the light and degrade the image recorded.

Launched in April 1990, NASA's Hubble Space Telescope has been delivering stunning images and making tremendous discoveries essentially by avoiding the blurring limitations imposed by observing through the Earth's atmosphere. A series of servicing missions performed by Space Shuttle astronauts have ensured that the Hubble Telescope has been continually equipped with a variety of advanced instruments, detectors and cameras. Exquisite Hubble Telescope imagery of stars is displayed in this book, together with examples from other great observatories such as the Spitzer Space Telescope. Named after the astrophysicist Lyman Spitzer, this telescope was placed in

ABOVE: *The William Herschel Telescope is located on the isolated peaks of Roque de Los Muchachos in the Canary Islands.*

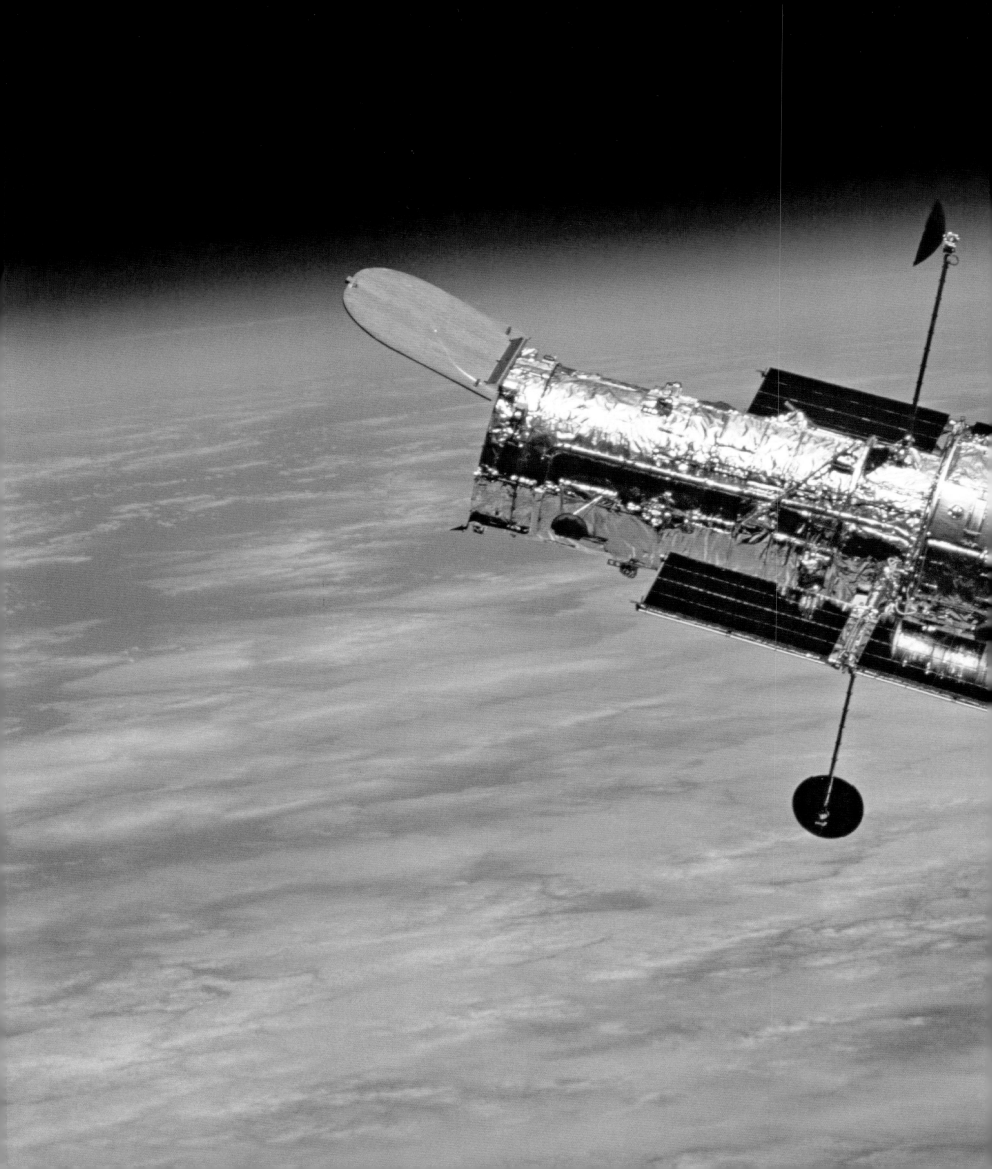

Earth-orbit in August 2003 with a primary mission of science due to last five years. The Spitzer Telescope is particularly important for studying the birth of stars and galaxies, during phases when they are mostly shrouded in clouds of cold dust that largely block out visible light, but not the infrared. At the other end of the spectrum, NASA also launched in July 1999 the Chandra X-ray observatory, named after the stellar astrophysicist Subrahmanyan Chandrasekhar. Designed to detect X-rays, this telescope together with the complementary deployment of the XMM-Newton telescope by the European Space Agency, presents unique opportunities to study the most energetic phenomena in the Universe.

Giant telescopes, with diameters of 10 metres (33 feet) or more, have made equally stunning discoveries over the past decade, from their vantage locations perched on mountain peaks on Earth. The twin Keck telescopes are located on the summit of the 4,200 metre (13,800 feet) Mauna Kea peak of the Hawaiian islands. Exploiting the stable, dry air of the upper atmosphere, and well away from the glare of city lights, each of the two telescopes has a primary light-gathering mirror composed of 36 hexagonal segments that combine to span 10 metres. Probing optical and partial infrared observations are also being conducted using a suite of telescopes operated by the European Southern Observatory at two mountainous sites in the Atacama desert region of Chile. The 8-metre (26 feet) class telescopes such as the Very Large Telescope (VLT) on the Paranal Mountain are pioneering studies that range from detecting the first galaxies assembled in the Universe to uncovering the subtlest evidence for planets orbiting around other stars. It is truly mouth-watering to think that the next generation of ground-based telescopes now being planned will have primary mirrors which are between 30 and 60 metres (100 and 200 feet) in diameter. Exploiting the most advanced technologies of the future will not be cheap and certainly requires funding pooled from large international collaborations. Another 21st-century innovation will be the Square Kilometre Array (SKA), which is currently priced at around 1.5 billion euros (2 billion US dollars). This ambitious and innovative radio astronomy facility involves 17 countries and aims to combine the signals from possibly hundreds of radio dishes spread over 1 million square-metres of collecting area. These remarkable new telescopes will not only extend our knowledge of the Universe, but they will undoubtedly uncover currently unknown phenomena.

LEFT: *The Hubble Space Telescope viewed during a servicing mission by astronauts onboard the Space Shuttle.*

Navigating the Stars

At first glance the clear night sky appears to be decorated by randomly scattered stellar dots. Since ancient times the cultures of the world have sought to bring greater order to the stars by sketching imaginary patterns in the sky and attributing them to Gods, mythical beasts and legends. We still recognise these constellations today in helping us to identify bright stars by breaking up the sky into more manageable portions. All societies created constellations, though most of those commonly used in the Northern Hemisphere have names derived from ancient Greek. Many of the constellations visible in the Southern Hemisphere were identified between the 16th and 18th centuries by sailors, navigators and astronomers such as Johnas Bayer (1572–1625). In the early 20th century the professional body of astronomers, known as the International Astronomical Union, formally adopted 38 modern constellations and together with the ancient well-established ones confirmed a total of 88 constellations. Sometimes the same constellation can be popularly known by several different names, such as Ursa Major, which is more familiar as the Plough to stargazers in the United Kingdom, but also known as the Big Dipper in North America, and was included in ancient mythology as the Great Bear to the Greeks, and the Jackal to the Egyptians.

The constellations remain important in modern astronomy as they provide a sense of organization to the sky and represent a basis for naming celestial bodies. The standard nomenclature for stars is that the brightest star in a constellation carries a 'proper name' that is usually derived from Arabic, such as Alderbaran or Betelgeuse. The stars also have Bayer designations in Greek alphabetical order to reflect their decreasing apparent brightness in the sky. Thus Betelgeuse, the brightest star in the constellation of Orion, is also known as alpha Orionis, and the second brightest star, Rigel, is beta Orionis. These, and a few other designations, only exist for the very brightest and easily visible stars.

In the 2nd century BC the Greek mathematician and astronomer Hipparchus (190–120 BC) grouped stars according to how bright they appeared in the sky. He assigned a system of magnitudes to them such that the brightest stars were labelled 1st magnitude and the faintest 6th magnitude. On a very dark night the dimmest stars visible to our unaided eyes are around 6th magnitude. This system is still in use today, but with a mathematical form that extends the magnitudes into negative numbers for the very brightest stars, which were not visible to Hipparchus from Greece. The magnitude scale also extends to larger positive numbers for very dim objects that can only be detected using telescopes. The brightest star in the night sky is Sirius, which has an apparent magnitude of about −1.5. On this scale the Sun has an apparent magnitude of −26.7 and the Full Moon has an apparent magnitude of

RIGHT: *Images of the Orion constellation, including its vast star-forming region, taken in the visible (*left panel*) and infrared (*right panel*) wave-bands.*

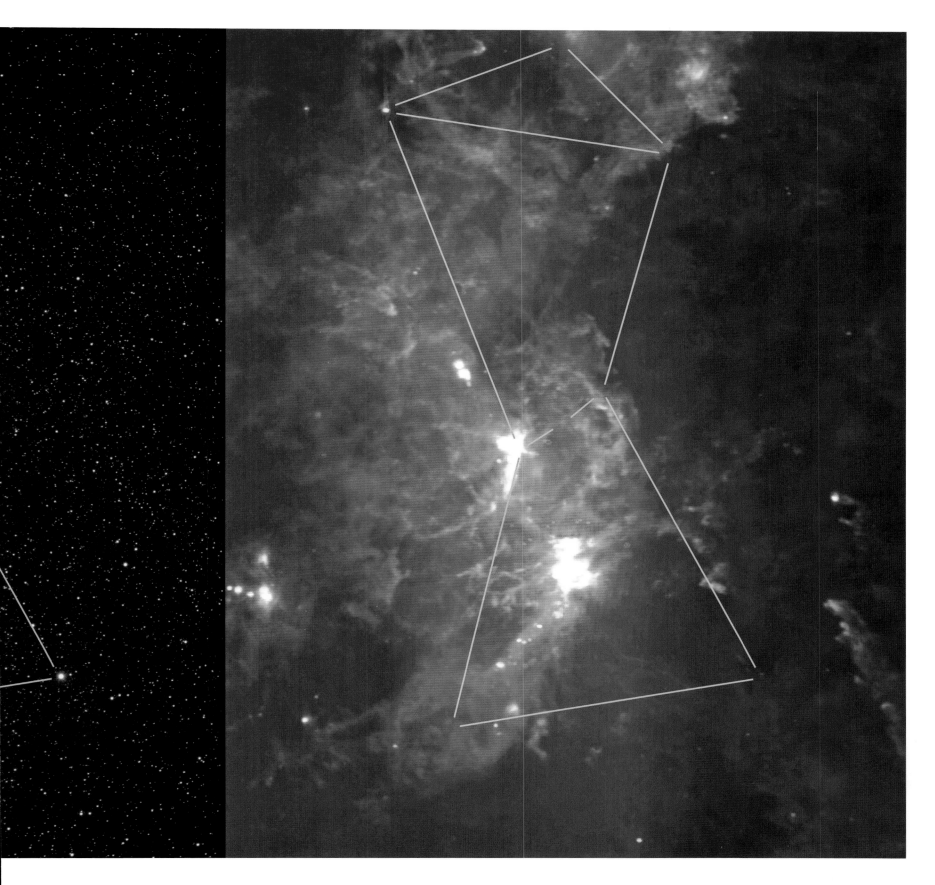

−12.6. The faintest objects detectable by instruments such as the Hubble Space Telescope and the twin Keck telescopes in Hawaii have apparent magnitudes as high as +30, which means they are almost 4 billion times fainter than the dimmest star that can be seen by the human eye alone. The numerous stars revealed through binoculars and telescopes are given catalogue names. The Henry Draper catalogue (named after the pioneering astrophotographer), contains almost 225,000 stars labelled 'HD', followed by a sequential number based on its position in the sky.

Cosmic Recycling

This book brings together some of the most detailed and remarkable images to reveal the intriguing story of a continuous cycle of star birth, evolution, death and re-birth. This is a process that is occurring across our Galaxy and every other nearby galaxy. All the stars we see in the sky will expire over millions and billions of years, but the scene will also be graced by a new generation of stars born out of giant nurseries in space that are loaded with gas and microscopic dust. In our lives we have only a fleeting time to capture a snap-shot of stars in the Universe, but this 'still portrait' contains an incredible variety of stars. We are able to witness stars of different sizes, masses, brightness, and ages and it is this rich cornucopia that has permitted astronomers to construct an understanding of the life stories of stars.

Hydrogen is not only the most abundant element in the Universe, it is the primary raw material for making stars and for providing a nuclear energy source that powers the stars. At its origin almost 14 billion years ago, the Universe contained primarily hydrogen and helium. Essentially all other chemical elements, including those we and the Earth are made from, were subsequently manufactured inside stars. This process is solely linked to the lives and deaths of stars. As stars approach their demise all the newly made chemical elements, including building blocks of life such as oxygen, carbon and silicon, are ejected out into space to become the new raw materials for making the next generation of stars and planets. We are thus witnessing a great cosmic cycle where new stars are assembled from the nuclear ashes of older stars. Numerous cycles of death and re-birth have occurred since the origin of the Universe and sometime in the distant future our Sun will also make its contribution by providing atoms that will be recycled to make new stars. Using our modern astronomical observatories we can today view stars of differing generations co-existing in grand galaxies and this makes it possible to conduct the most probing studies of the Universe.

As the chapters of this book unfold, all the significant phases in the lives of stars are revealed, together with their pivotal roles in shaping structures that range from planets to galaxies. The aim of the book is to transform and advance your view of stars so that they no longer appear as anonymous twinkling specs, but as remarkable celestial bodies that have histories and lives stretching over billions of years. Each time you then look at the night sky you will be reminded of the great acts of creation, luminous power, and cataclysmic demise that are being played out in space.

RIGHT: *A 70-light-year diameter bubble of gas and dust which is spawning the birth of new stars along its dense edges.*

BELOW: *Ultraviolet image from NASA's Galex orbiter reveals a 13-light-year long chain of material blown away from the star Mira over a time span of almost 39,000 years.*

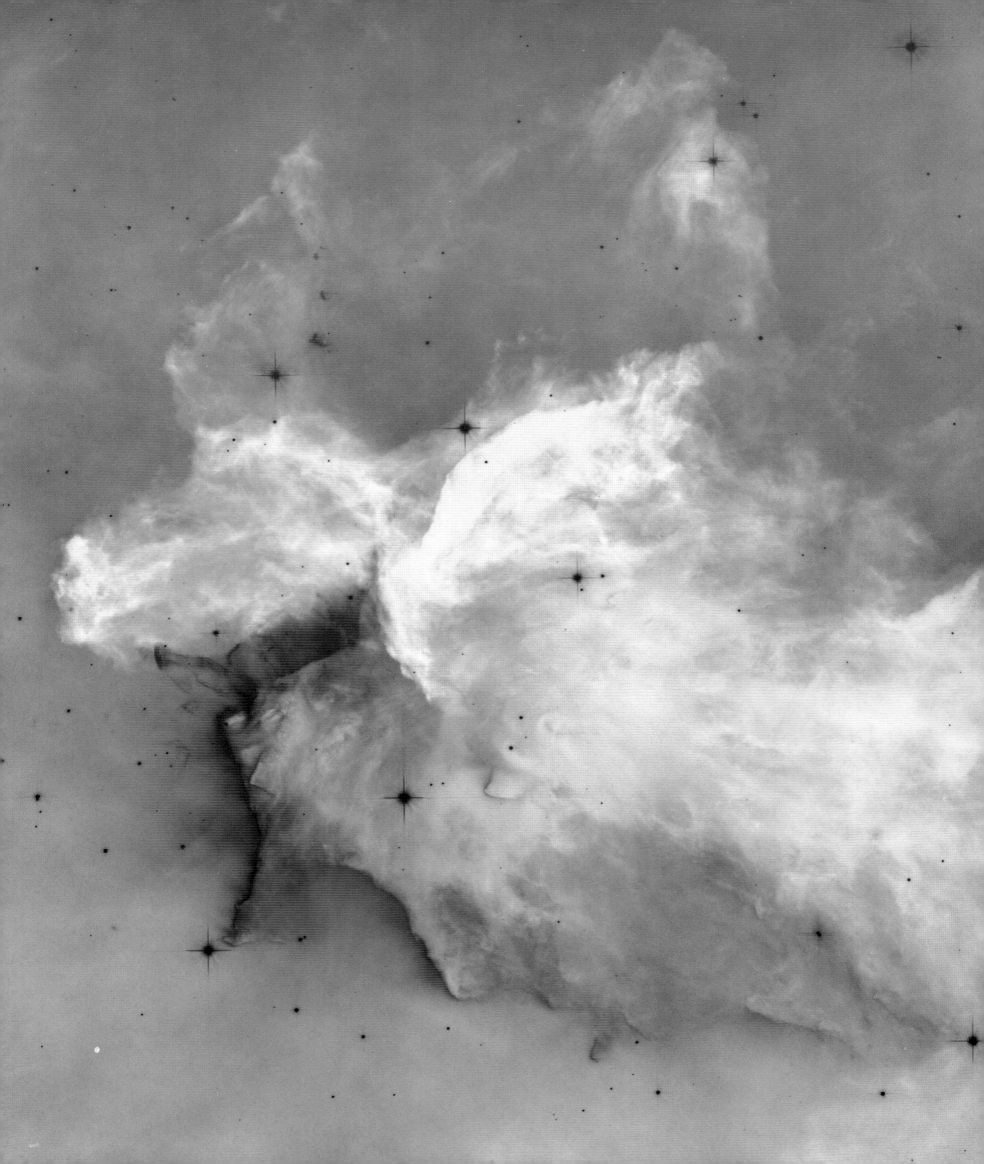

Part one

DUSTY BIRTH

Reservoirs in Space

The space between stars in a galaxy is almost a vacuum, but it is not entirely empty. Known as the interstellar medium, a diffuse 'soup' of gas and dust pervades the vast regions between the stars. Here lies the source of raw materials – including abundant hydrogen gas and microscopic dust particles, from which new stars are formed.

On average, matter in the interstellar medium is very thinly spread, with barely one atom in a cubic centimetre of space. That makes it sparser than even the most advanced vacuum systems in our laboratories on Earth. However, because the volume of interstellar space in a galaxy is so large compared to the volume occupied by stars, the seemingly insignificant content of the interstellar medium can, in total, add up to almost 10 per cent of the mass of a spiral-shaped galaxy such as ours.

On the face of it, gas in space that is so tenuously distributed cannot possibly be gathered by the action of gravity to make stars. What saves us is that the interstellar medium is in fact very lumpy and turbulent. Regions where the matter is more concentrated are called nebulae. These clouds of gas and dust can have different conditions, such as temperatures and densities. The prolific ultraviolet radiation emitted by nearby luminous young stars may be absorbed by the nebulae, causing the gas in them to heat and emit radiation in regions visible to the human eye. These regions of warmed up hydrogen gas often appear in our telescopes as beautiful reddish-coloured glowing areas. Other nebulae are very dark, and are made up of cool dust particles that totally block the light from the stars behind them. The Horsehead nebulae in the constellation of Orion is a striking example of a dark nebula that is only visible because it is silhouetted against a hotter light-emitting gas cloud behind it.

LEFT: *Star-making clouds of gas and dust are revealed in this Hubble Telescope image of a spiral galaxy called NGC1672.*

Giant Clouds of Molecules

The perfect breeding grounds for the birth of new stars are considerably larger and cooler regions of interstellar space known as giant molecular clouds. These puffy agglomerations of molecules are the largest inhabitants of galaxies, with diameters ranging from about one light-year to almost 300 light-years. An individual giant cloud can contain enough gas to form more than 100,000 stars like our Sun. A well-developed spiral galaxy such as our Milky Way Galaxy can host up to 2,000 giant molecular clouds. Their great size means that most of the gas within the clouds is well shielded from the ultraviolet light of surrounding stars, and so their temperatures can get as low as –260 degrees Celsius (–440 degrees Fahrenheit). The molecular clouds are thus too cold to emit optical light, but they do emit radio waves that can be detected by radio telescopes on Earth. Following their discovery by this method almost 25 years ago, astronomers have mapped the spread of star-forming clouds across our Milky Way Galaxy, and in doing so have also traced the spiral-shaped layout of the Galaxy.

The cold conditions within the giant clouds allow vast amounts of hydrogen molecules to form, together with other molecules such as water, carbon monoxide and ammonia. More complex species that comprise the basic building blocks of life may also be present, including, for example, methanol and ethyl alcohol. Loaded with raw materials for making stars, individual giant molecular clouds are constantly agitated and stirred up. Their turbulent interiors may be disturbed by gravitational effects caused by collisions between clouds, or by a passing shock wave from the supernova explosion of a nearby massive star that has reached the end of its life.

These disturbances can act to trigger the process of star formation in the giant clouds. A gravitational imbalance induces the cloud to collapse and compress. As the density in parts of the cloud rises, the vast structure will start to fragment and form clumps. These clumps may in turn collapse and fragment further to form even smaller, denser clumps. In this manner, the giant molecular clouds will form numerous small patches, each of which contains enough matter to form multiple star systems.

The small, compressed fragments found within a giant cloud are called dense cores. New stars are formed inside these dense cores. In order for a dense core to collapse into a star, the gravitational forces compressing it inwards must be greater than the pressure of the gas pushing outwards. The conditions in the core are ideal for this to happen since the density of material is high, while at the same time the temperatures are very low, so gas pressure is very weak.

RIGHT: *A combined visible, infrared and ultraviolet composite image of the beautiful M81 spiral galaxy, revealing powerful episodes of new star formation.*

Once the gravitational collapse has truly started, the core shrinks and becomes even denser, which in turn further increases the gravitational force pulling the gas inwards, and the process self-cycles in this manner. The energy of the falling gas particles is converted into heat energy, and so eventually the temperature of the now extremely dense core starts to rise. The gas becomes warm enough to produce infrared and microwave radiation, thus giving astronomers the first glimpse of the earliest stages in the birth of stars.

Using infrared telescopes, we can glean information about the temperature and density within a collapsing region, and determine how fast the core is collapsing. Infrared and radio observations can also tell us which molecules are present in the star-making clouds. Over a few million years, the shrinking and now very dense core grows as it attracts in-falling matter, and its internal temperature increases rapidly. Eventually, with the central temperature approaching 15 million degrees Celsius (27 million degrees Fahrenheit), thermonuclear fusion begins in what is now the core of a newborn star. The greater the mass, the faster the star is born. A Sun-like star would take about ten million years to emerge from the original gas cloud, while a star ten times more massive will be assembled in barely 100,000 years (which is a very short time period in stellar astronomy). Currently, in our Milky Way Galaxy, material that is about three times the Sun's mass worth is being converted into new stars every year. A single fragmented giant molecular cloud, hosting numerous dense cores, can yield several thousand stars, found in prolific clusters (*see Open and Globular Clusters, page 58, in Clustered Siblings*).

The ultimate fate of the original giant molecular cloud can vary depending on its environment within a galaxy. In most isolated cases, less than 50 per cent of the gas in a giant cloud will be used to make up stars. The rest of the nascent material will be dispersed and blown away by the strong radiation and winds of matter that is expelled by the newly formed stars.

Emerging stellar nurseries are among the most spectacular sights in space, and tremendous new insights and views of star-forming clouds have been provided in recent years by probing telescopes such as the Hubble Space Telescope and NASA's Spitzer Infrared Space Telescope. In the remainder of this chapter, we will take a closer look at some of the stunning individual examples that reside not just in our Galaxy, but also in more distant locations beyond.

The Rising Eagle

A striking example of a nearby star-forming giant molecular cloud is the Eagle Nebula. This rich reservoir lies about 7,000 light-years away in the constellation of Serpens, close to the border of Sagittarius. It nests in the inner spiral arm to the Sun's in the Milky Way Galaxy. The Eagle Nebula is home to a diverse array of objects, including clusters of very young, hot stars; clouds that are in the process of forming new stars; glowing interstellar gas; and light-obscuring microscopic dust. The nebula extends over a diameter of more than 50 light-years, and surrounds a central cluster of stars that includes members that are less than one million years old; these members are extremely youthful compared, for example, to the five-billion-year age of the Sun today.

A remarkable close-up view of part of the Eagle Nebula was captured by the Wide-Field and Planetary Camera onboard the Hubble Space Telescope. Known as the 'pillars of creation', three dark, cold columns of gas and dust were revealed silhouetted against the glowing background of warmer nebular material. The light-year-tall pillars rise from an inner dark molecular cloud like stalagmites from the floor of a cave. The sharp Hubble images provide detailed insights into the earliest processes of assembling stars. The heads of the three vast stellar incubators are illuminated by the strong ultraviolet radiation from nearby infant stars. In a process called photo-evaporation, the stellar radiation 'boils' away gas along the surface of the pillars, thus sculpting them and uncovering denser egg-like globules of gas. The globules appear as 'fingers' extending from the surface of the pillars, each barely the size of our solar system. These 'fingers' are thought to cocoon newly formed stars that

RIGHT: *False-colour view from the Spitzer Telescope of the Eagle nebula, which is loaded with prolific stellar nurseries.*

have yet to fully blow away the remnant material of gas and dust that surrounds them. The globules mark one of the earliest stages in the evolution of stars, and our own Sun was likely born in a structure such as this.

The intriguing dusty pillars of the Eagle Nebula have attracted not just the gaze of the Hubble Space Telescope, but also other powerful observatories that are tuned to study objects at non-visible wavebands such as X-rays and infrared. NASA's Chandra X-ray observatory, in orbit around the Earth, has revealed that very few X-rays are being emitted by the pillars themselves. This suggests that many of the stars embedded in the finger-like globules protruding from the pillars are still too young to generate strong X-rays. Toward the other, lower energy end of the electromagnetic spectrum, images from the Spitzer Infrared Observatory suggest that the pillars are being

eroded further by the blast wave of a nearby supernova explosion. These eerie structures might already have started to disintegrate due to the bombardment from the supernova event, and their demise may be complete in just a thousand years or so.

The Eagle Nebula is host to a second equally remarkable structure that is a vast incubator for newborn stars: a soaring, dusty sculpture of gas and dust has been imaged by the Hubble Space Telescope, with a span of almost 9.5 light-years. Stars are thought to be forming inside this stellar 'spire', under the inducement of a nearby cluster of young stars that provide intense starlight and energy to heat the dark hydrogen clouds. Telltale signatures of star birth are once more provided by clumps and fingers of material, inside which dense, cold gas has started an inevitable collapse under its own weight.

ABOVE: Spitzer infrared image of pillars being sculpted by radiation and winds from massive stars in the Eagle Nebula.

RIGHT: The dense tower of gas and dust known as the 'stellar spire' is revealed here residing in the Eagle nebula.

The Great Nebula in Orion

One of the most splendid star-forming clouds in the sky can be readily seen through a large pair of binoculars or a modest telescope. Following down the 'sword' in the constellation of Orion, it is possible to see a fuzzy patch surrounding the star known as Theta Orionis. The patch was first described as a nebula in 1610, just one year after Italian scientist Galileo Galilei's (1564–1642) initial use of the telescope. Following centuries of observations, the Orion Nebula is today established as one of the nearest regions to Earth where stars have been made over the past 300,000 years or so – very recent in astronomical time-scales. At a relatively short distance of 1,500 light-years, the Orion Nebula is an astoundingly beautiful and valuable laboratory for the study of star birth.

In 2005, the Hubble Space Telescope acquired one of the most detailed images ever acquired of the Orion Nebula, assembled from data taken over 105 Earth orbits of the spacecraft. The observations provided unique access to the star-forming history, from dense dark blobs of matter to gas pillars, and even to plate-like swirls of material orbiting around young stars, which could be the foundries of new planet systems. The rich red and green hues of the nebula are due to interstellar gas – mainly hydrogen and oxygen – glowing as it basks in the strong ultraviolet radiation from young stars that have completed their birth and are now generating their own energy from nuclear reactions in their central cores.

A substantial amount of the energy needed to keep the Orion Nebula radiating its colours is attributed to a small cluster of very young, hot stars called the Trapezium. Located in the brightest part of the Orion Nebula, the luminous Trapezium stars outshine all other stellar members of this cloud, including a swarm of almost 1,000 much fainter stars that have lower (Sun-like) masses. The Trapezium stars play a fundamental role in sculpting the surrounding nebula through a stream of energetic gas particles known as a stellar wind. These outflows of matter are considerably more powerful than the wind from our own Sun. The collision of the stellar winds with the surrounding gas and dust of the nebula creates cavities and erodes the dense clumps that are incubators for new star formation. The shock waves from the strong outflows from young stars can also act to squeeze clouds of gas together and trigger their collapse under gravity toward the creation of stars.

The winds from the massive Trapezium stars may even be powerful enough to ultimately disperse and erode the Orion Nebula itself, perhaps making it disappear from our view in 100,000 years or so. This would mean that one of the most iconic objects in space, the Horsehead Nebula, will also slowly disperse. Today, this remarkable dusty cloud in Orion coincidentally traces out the shape of a horse's head, projected against a background of glowing gases. The light-obscuring Horsehead itself is made up of cigarette-smoke-sized dark, sooty particles. Over many thousands of years, the great nebula in Orion will erode to leave behind a cluster of young, hot stars, producing intense ultraviolet radiation. The cluster would resemble one that is, for example, currently on view in the constellation of Pleiades.

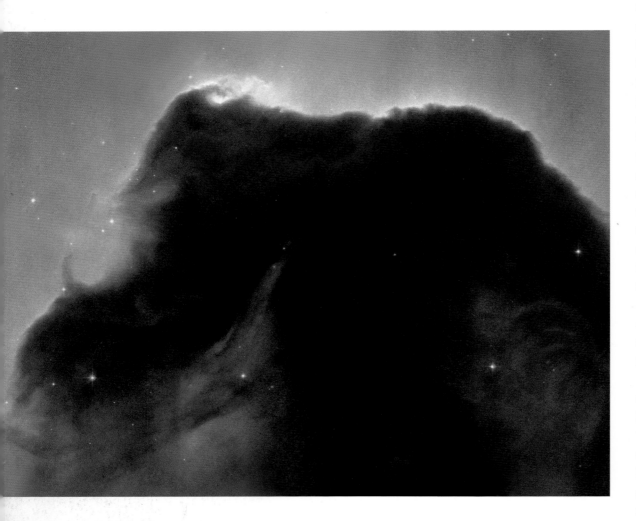

ABOVE: *A detailed view of the Horsehead nebula in Orion.*

RIGHT: *A false-colour composite of infrared images showing the heart of the turbulent star-forming Orion nebula.*

Distant Nurseries

The tremendous amount of power possessed by modern astronomical observatories such as the Hubble and Spitzer Space telescopes and the 10-metre-diameter (33 feet) ground-based telescopes have made it possible to study not only the birth of stars in our Galaxy, but also in other, more distant, extra-galactic settings. This leap into other galaxies is founded on the light-gathering power of very large telescopes and other sophisticated instrumentation that can deliver images of astounding high definition and clarity. This sharp vision means that the intricate details of star-forming clouds can be discerned at great distances beyond our own galaxy.

Astronomers can combine information from different wavebands (such as optical, ultraviolet, radio and infrared) to explore other galaxies where the conditions for star birth may be very different from what we see locally. For example, the formation of a star may proceed extremely rapidly, in essence allowing the evolution of the galaxy itself to be understood. While some galaxies may assemble stars much more quickly than our Milky Way Galaxy, other galaxies might be totally devoid of star birth. The ultimate quest is to obtain information about the formation and evolution of galaxies throughout the Universe, including the vast bursts of star birth that are predicted to have occurred in the earliest times in the age of the Universe.

About 210,000 light-years away, toward the southern constellation of Tucana, lies the Small Magellanic Cloud.

ABOVE: *The stunning star-formation region known as LH95, which is located about 160,000 light-years away in the Large Magellanic Cloud.*

RIGHT: *Newly formed stars are ejecting powerful winds of matter to sculpt the surrounding NGC602 nebula in the Small Magellanic Cloud.*

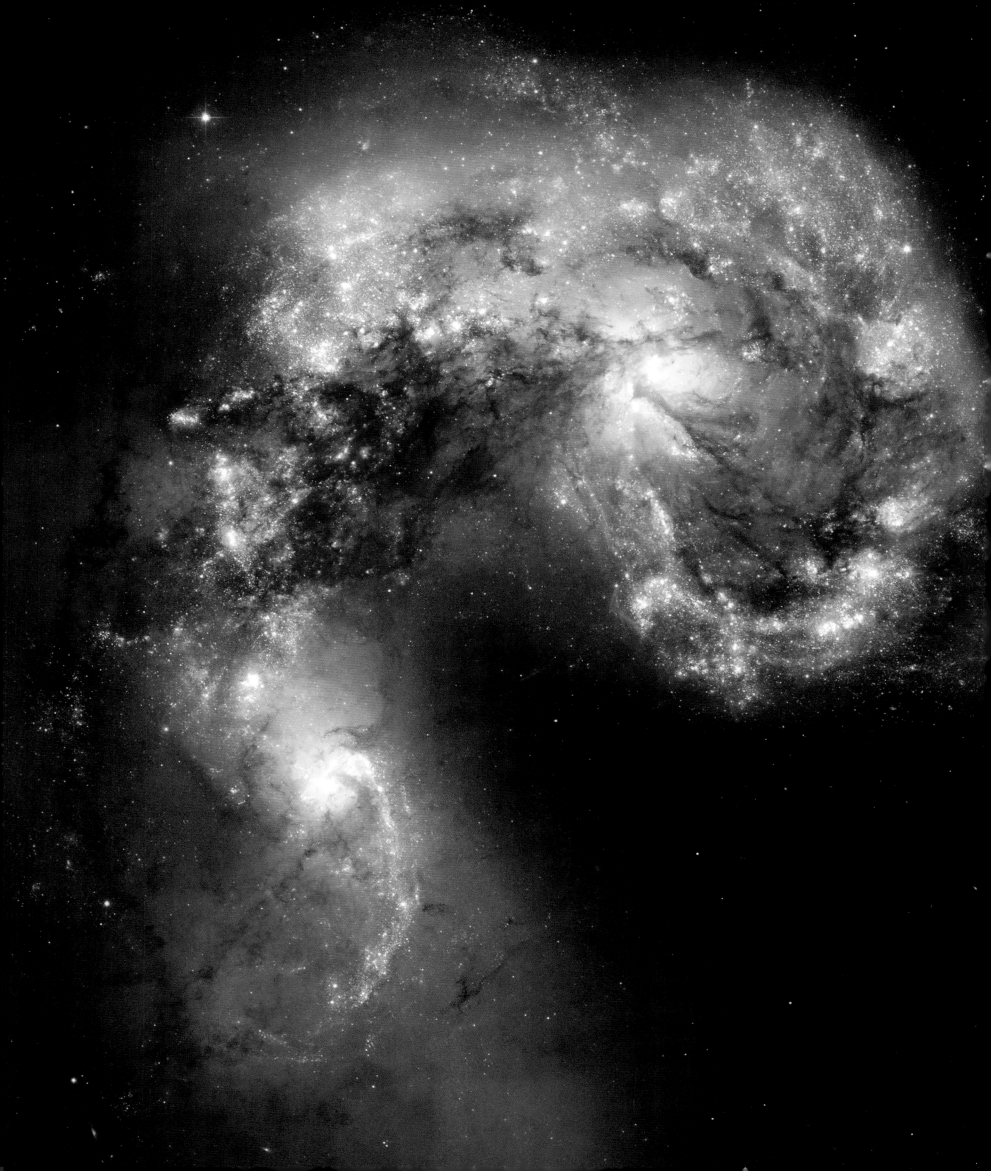

One of our closest galactic neighbours, it is an irregular shaped galaxy, with a diameter about a third of that of the Milky Way Galaxy. The Small Magellanic Cloud has undergone prolific outbursts of rapid star formation, giving rise to numerous powerful young stars. The relative proximity of this small galaxy to ours, and the fact that it contains a much lower percentage of heavier chemical elements such as carbon, nitrogen and oxygen, makes the Small Magellanic Cloud a fantastic analog for studying the process of star birth in the earliest epochs of the Universe.

One outstanding example of star birth in the Small Magellanic Cloud is known as NGC602, where the rise of infant stars has been captured in detailed imagery. A bright central cluster of stars is providing the radiation and shock waves to sculpt the surrounding nebula of gas and dust. One consequence of this erosion and compression is the triggering of new star formation in the ridges of the nebula. Powerful ejections from young stars have shaped pillars of gas and dust in the outer regions of the nebula, and it is here that the latest episodes of star birth are now thought to be taking place.

The youngest galaxies formed at the earliest times of the Universe are too faint and distant for us to study them directly, even with large telescopes. Astronomers therefore hunt for other galaxies in the nearby Universe that might have similar properties to those assembled at the earliest epochs. The best candidates are the close-by dwarf galaxies, which are deficient in chemical elements heavier than hydrogen and helium. A particularly energetic example is NGC4449, which is located about 12.5 million light-years from us, toward the constellation of Canes Venatici. Images taken in the optical and infrared wavebands reveal intense and widespread formation of stars occurring throughout NGC4449. Indeed, its bursts of star birth are so prolific that, if continued at the current rate, all of the gas available for making stars in this dwarf galaxy would be consumed in a billion years or so. NGC4449 is also unusual in that active regions of star birth are not just confined to the central parts, but extend out across much of the galaxy. The images even reveal massive dark, dusty clouds that will become the sites for future episodes of star formation.

Another phenomenal setting for distant stellar nurseries is provided when two galaxies collide in space. More than half of the galaxies in the Universe are predicted to have undergone one or more collisions with other galaxies. These great cosmic interactions were much more common in the early times of the Universe, when the galaxies were much closer to each other and therefore more likely to come together under the influence of their gravitational attraction. However, since the space between the stars in a galaxy is so large, and the galaxies are thus so empty, the stars themselves almost never impact into each other when two galaxies collide. The same is not true, however, for the vast clouds of gases and dust that reside between the stars. The giant interstellar clouds of the two galaxies will come into contact, with the effect of compressing the clouds and increasing the pressure within them. As the density and shocks increase, the effects can be dramatic. The squeezed gas clouds fragment and the galaxy collision in effect triggers bursts of new star formation.

A spectacular example of rampant star birth in a pair of colliding galaxies can be witnessed in the spiral-shaped Antennae galaxies, which started to gravitationally interact a few hundred million years ago. Details of the star formation process initiated by this collision have been captured using the Advanced Camera for Surveys onboard the Hubble Space Telescope. The central regions of the original galaxies contain collections of mostly old stars that appear as orange blobs on the images. The new sites of active star formation are clearly seen as numerous blue regions, each of which is a cluster of young stars barely a million years old. The energy from these bright, hot stars makes the surrounding hydrogen gas glow in hues of pink.

It is expected that most of the young star clusters triggered into birth by the interaction of the two Antennae galaxies will spread apart and disperse in time, thus introducing new stars throughout the merging galaxies. The collision on view represents a great cosmic laboratory for understanding how stars are assembled from giant interstellar clouds. Some of the individual knots of stars seen in the Antennae galaxies contain vast samples of stars, with a total mass of more than 10 million times that of the Sun. As we will see later on in this book, the ability to witness vast numbers of young stars gives astronomers valuable opportunities for studying super-star clusters and the rise of the most massive stars in galaxies.

LEFT: *Hubble Space Telescope image of the merging pair of Antennae galaxies, where the collision is giving rise to the formation of dense new superstar clusters.*

Birth Rings and Jets

The final stages in the formation of stars are marked by some fascinating and very significant structures. We have already seen that all stars, including our Sun, formed from a vast cloud of gas and dust in space, which contracts in on itself under the action of its own gravitational pull. Following the 18th-century hypothesis of Immanuel Kant (1724–1804) and Marquis de Laplace (1749–1827), scientists have predicted that the original spinning nebula would evolve initially into a young star surrounded by a plate-like revolving disk of gas and dust. The disk is today referred to as a proto-planetary disk, since it is thought to contain the dusty raw material out of which planets are assembled.

A profound aspect of this theory is that the formation of planets is a natural consequence of the birth of stars. The initial gravitational collapse of an enormous interstellar cloud of gas and dust leads to a very dense and hot central condensation, which becomes the star. The leftover material not used to make the star forms a surrounding spinning disk; the spinning disk forms because, as the original cloud collapses and becomes smaller, it spins faster and faster. This process is known as the conservation of angular momentum, and is similar to the way in which an ice skater pulls in her arms and legs to perform a rapid spin. If the collapsing material has too much angular momentum it cannot fall directly onto the new born star, and goes instead into an orbit around the central massive object. Eventually, this remnant material forms a plate-like disk in the equatorial plane of the star. As we will see in this chapter, the debris of dust and gas in the disk may be cleared away after millions of years by the effects of strong jets and winds of material expelled by the infant star.

LEFT: *Powerful jets of gas ejected by the infant star HH 46/47 slam into surrounding matter to create two vast bubbles.*

Dusty Disks

Today, the study of the disks around young stars is driven by a desire to understand not only the origin of stars, but also the formation of planetary systems. Gradually, over tens of millions of years, the tiny dust grains within the disk collide with each other and stick together. In a hierarchal build-up, the larger grains then combine to slowly grow into asteroid-sized bodies, eventually forming moon-sized planetary embryos. The rocky terrestrial planets in our solar system are large gatherings of these types of bodies. The giant gas planets, such as Jupiter and Saturn, formed in the cooler and icier regions of the disk further from the young Sun, where it was possible to make much larger rocky cores of planets. These giant trigger nuclei, possibly 20 times the mass of the Earth, had substantial gravitational pull, and thus accumulated vast envelopes of mostly hydrogen and helium gas to form the extended atmospheres that characterize the gas planets.

Astronomers are keen to detect the planet-founding disks around newborn stars. The disks are very faint compared to the light output of the central star, but nevertheless, just as the number of detected exoplanets has steadily increased over recent years, so too has the number of disks imaged around stars. A variety of observational techniques are used to see them, including direct techniques such as the utilization of sensitive cameras onboard the Hubble and Spitzer Space telescopes. It is also an advantage to observe the disks at infrared and millimetre wavebands, as opposed to the optical (visible) regions, since the former are more effective at probing through the dust that usually shrouds newborn stars. Another very effective approach is to simultaneously observe a stellar object with two or more co-ordinated telescopes. Known as interferometry, the power of this method is that it allows astronomers to study disk structures with the same image resolution that would be delivered by a single telescope that had a mirror as large as the separation of the individual telescopes being combined. The goal is that by studying a wide variety of disks, we can collect 'snapshots' that can be compared to

RIGHT: *An artist's illustration of a young star surrounded by a swirling dusty disk which contains raw materials for building planets.*

help unravel the evolution in time of the last stages in the formation of stars and the rise of planets.

An example of a young star known to be surrounded by a vast reservoir of planet-building materials is the relatively dim red object known as AU Microscopii, lying more than 30 light-years away in the southern constellation of Microscopium. With an estimated age of 12 million years, AU Microscopii is about 400 times younger than our Sun, and is thought to be in an active phase of building planets. Visible and infrared images of the star captured by the Hubble and Spitzer telescopes, along with the giant Keck II telescopes on Mauna Kea, in Hawaii, have revealed a debris disk of dusty matter with an outer radius of almost 210 times the Earth-to-Sun distance. That makes the disk larger than the size of the orbit of Neptune. The disk is viewed almost edge-on, somewhat like looking at a dinner plate from a sideways perspective. The light from the young star reflects off the microscopic dust grains in the disk, most of which are probably debris from collisions between larger bodies, such as asteroids and comets.

Given the young age of AU Microscopii, it seems that planets in its disk are still at the phases of gathering mass. This process can be witnessed by the presence of structures that are sculpted into the disk by hidden planetary bodies. For example, the infrared images in particular reveal an uneven disk with clumps, which are thought to arise due to the gravity of the unseen planets. The relative proximity to us of AU Microscopii makes it an excellent target for more detailed and sensitive investigation by the next generation of instrumentation and telescopes.

In contrast, a near face-on view of a planet debris disk is seen encircling the yellow dwarf star known as HD 107146. Almost 88 light-years from us, this star is very similar to the Sun in surface temperature and size. It is, however, estimated to be less than 250 million years old, which is very youthful compared to our Sun's age of almost 5 billion years. The outer radius of the disk around HD 107146 extends beyond 100 times the Earth-to-Sun distance, and analysis of the images suggests that most of the structure is made up of microscopic

dust grains. The nearest comparative structure currently in our solar system is the debris of cometary material and dust that lies in the Kuiper Belt, just beyond the orbit of Neptune. One possible reason for the largely extended disk seen in HD 107146 is that it marks an earlier phase in the evolution of our solar system: perhaps our solar system also had a disk with 10,000 times more dust when it was barely 250 million years old. On the other hand, current theories suggest it is highly unlikely that a young Kuiper Belt could shrink, narrow and lose dust by such a magnitude to evolve from a disk like the one in HD 107146 to what we see in our solar system today. If it were true that HD 107146 is unlikely to slowly change into a planetary system like ours, then these observations would intriguingly show that two apparently very similar stars may have had rather different birth histories.

Another stunning pancake-like structure made of rock, dust and ice has been discovered around a newborn star called Fomalhaut. This very bright star is about twice the mass of the Sun, and only 25 light-years distant in the constellation of Pisces Australis. Images taken in the infrared waveband have been complemented by sharp visible light exposures from the Hubble Space Telescope. Fomalhaut is less than 5 per cent of the age of the Sun, and thus it offers another excellent laboratory for studying the processes that may have been occurring during the early stages of the formation of our solar system.

The environment around Fomalhaut is likely to be a violent one, with prolific bombardment and collisions between asteroid-sized bodies, giving rise to pulverized dusty remnants. The ring has a diameter of 280 times the Earth-to-Sun distance, making it four times wider than the Kuiper Belt in our solar system. Oddly, the centre of Fomalhaut's ring is highly offset from the position of the star. One possible explanation for this misalignment is that an unseen planet is orbiting the star in an elliptical path and reshaping the inner regions of the ring due to its gravitational pull. The inner edge of the ring appears sharp in the images, which is consistent with the notion that a planet is acting in a plough-like manner to clear and sculpt the debris material.

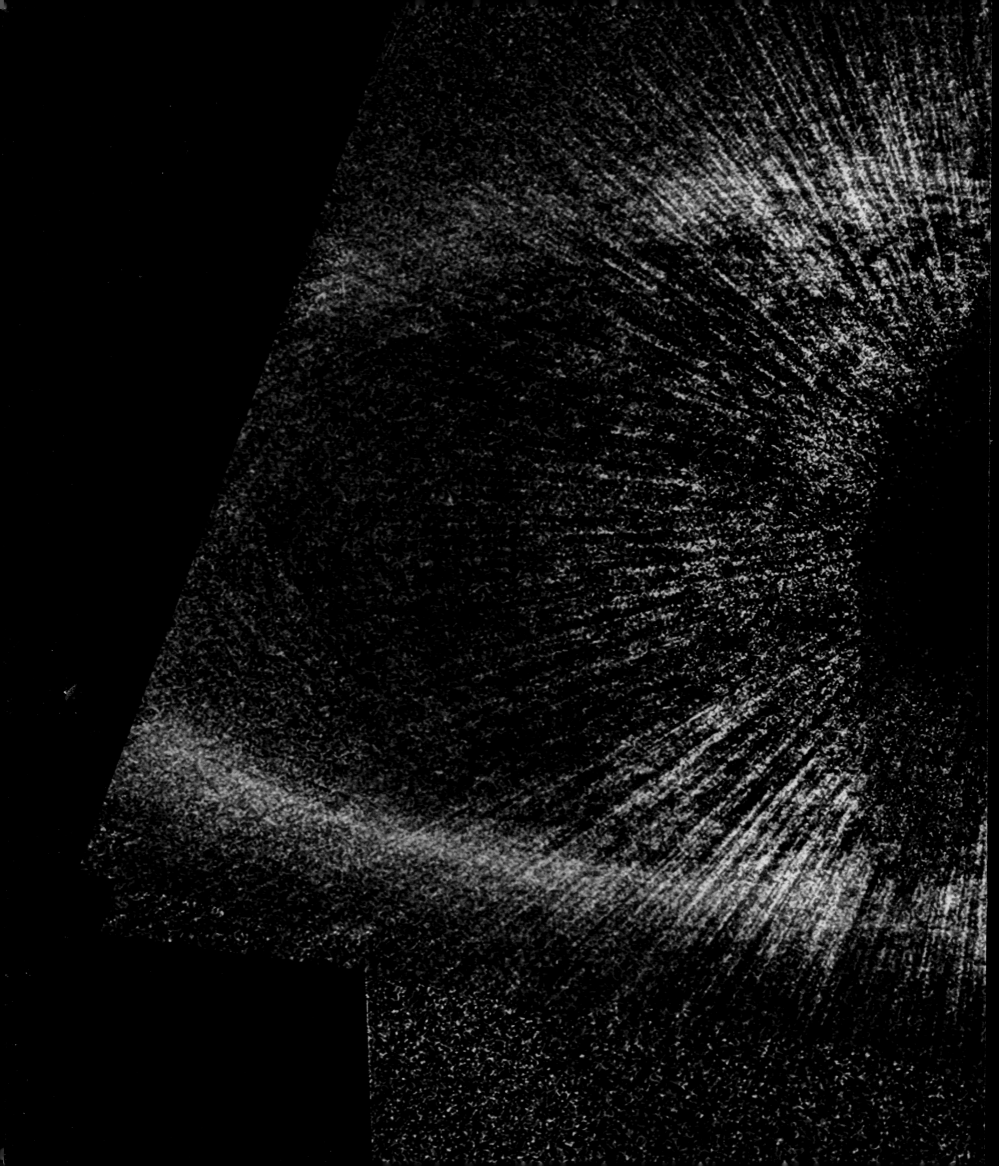

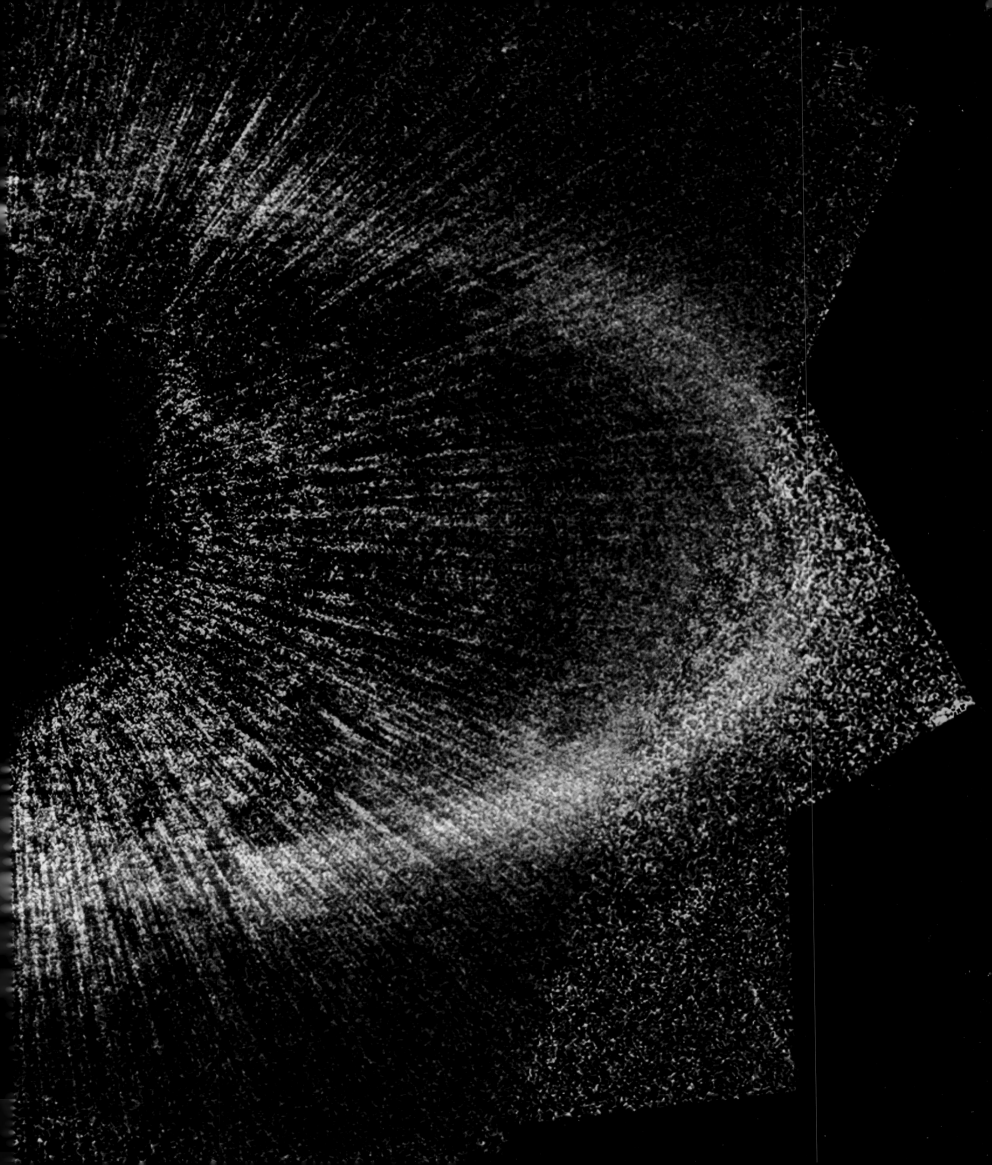

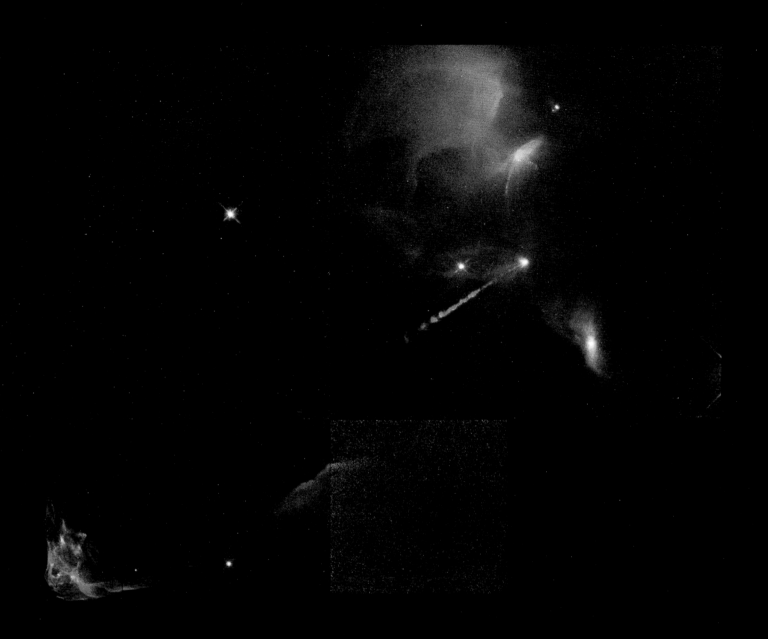

Outflows of Gas

Just as swirling dusty rings and disks are an integral part of the process by which stars are made, so too are the blowtorch-like flows of gas that stream away from newly formed stars. Furious jets of hot gas are driven out from deep within infant stellar objects, and clumps of matter can be ejected at speeds of almost 500,000 kilometres per hour (310,700 miles per hour).

Very young stars provide the ideal settings for investigating the nature of the outflows, or winds of gas, that are pushed away from astronomical objects. Similar phenomena can be witnessed as well in various other settings in space, some of which are much more extreme and powerful, such as the centres of very active galaxies or an ordinary star orbiting very closely around a black hole. The study of outflows as one of the manifestations of the birth of a star is thus important not just in understanding the origins of stars; this knowledge can also be applied to many other classes of bodies.

During the 1950s, astronomers George Herbig (b.1920) and Guillermo Haro (1913–1988) independently discovered small, compact clouds of gas that appeared to be linked to the sites in which the formation of stars was actively taking place. These bright patches appeared as glowing nebulae, often occurring in pairs on either side of a very young star. Observations made over the following decades revealed that these objects were in fact narrow jets of gas powered by the newly formed stars, and that these narrow streams of gas are moving away from the stellar source at speeds of between 100 to more than 1,000 kilometres per second (62 to 620 miles per second). Known today as Herbig–Haro (HH) objects, over 400 individual cases have been discovered so far, but astronomers predict that numerous more Herbig–Haro objects await discovery in our Galax.

ABOVE: *Bubbles and jets of gas ejected from the newly formed Herbig–Haro star HH–34.*

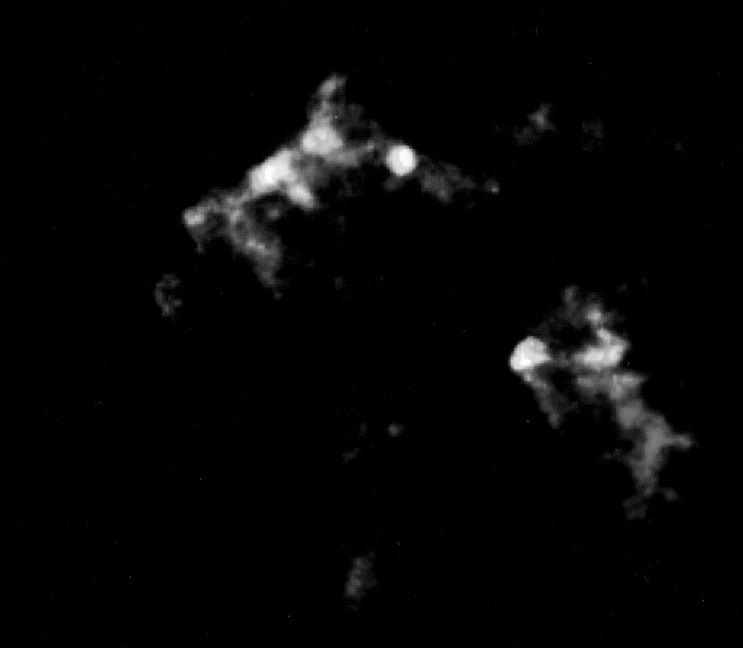

The current study of outflows from very young stars is conducted using telescope observations made at various wavebands, including X-ray, ultraviolet, visible and infrared. The Hubble Space Telescope in particular has revealed a number of spectacular examples, some of which are highlighted in this section.

The rushing jets of matter that are expelled by the star can be more than 10 light-years long in some cases, though the total amount of mass ejected may be barely 30 times the mass of the Earth. Since the jets are so narrowly confined, the gas within them is densely packed and is heated to temperatures of about 9700 degrees Celsius (17,500 degrees Fahrenheit). Herbig–Haro objects are rather dim, however, and detailed observations of them demand the use of large, powerful telescopes. Since the formation of stars out of giant clouds of gas mostly results in close clusters of many newborn systems, the Herbig–Haro jets also tend to be discovered in groups or associations.

There remain uncertainties in our understanding of precisely how the young stars are able to power and eject the prolific jets of matter seen in Herbig–Haro objects. The generally accepted view is that the outflows are connected to the disk of material that swirls around new stars. The gas in the disk is spiralling inwards, and thus the innermost regions of the disk, close to the star, get very hot. The rapidly spinning inner part of the disk is also connected to strong magnetic fields that uncoil like a spring. The combined effect is to lift material perpendicular to the disk and accelerate it into jets arising from the two poles of the star. The jets also act as brakes on the disk itself, slowing its spin rate, which in turn allows more matter to fall directly onto the growing star. The jets therefore play an important role in the birth of the star.

A fascinating example of a powerful jet can be found almost 450 light-years away in the Chamaeleon I star-forming cloud, which is home to about a hundred or so

ABOVE: *Clouds of gas known as Herbig–Haro 2 are heated by the blast of jets due to high speed gas ejected from a newborn star.*

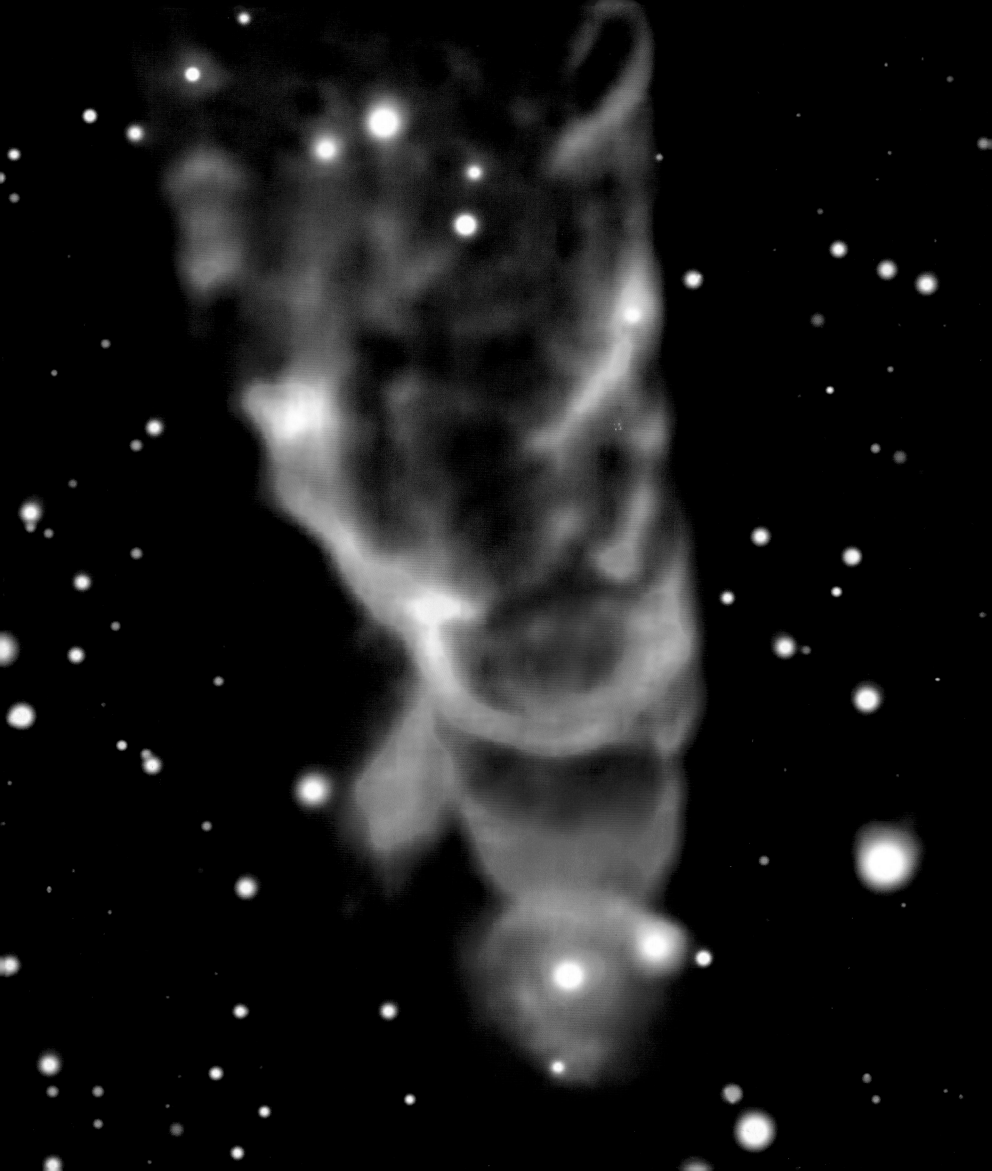

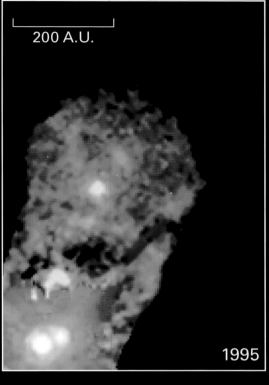

1995

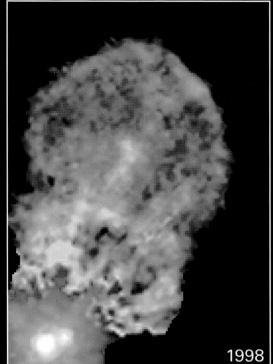

1998

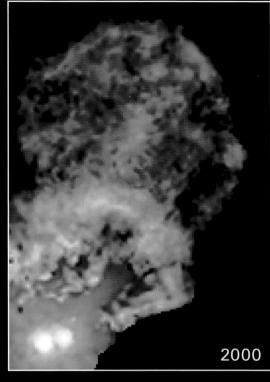

2000

ABOVE: *Hubble Telescope images secured over 5 years reveal the expanding bubble of gas blown out by the young stellar system XZ Tauri.*

LEFT: *Spitzer Telescope infrared image of a powerful jet flowing away from a newly formed star and ploughing through interstellar gas and dust. The resultant tornado-like feature is known as Herbig–Haro 49/50.*

young stars. Labelled Herbig–Haro 49/50, the Spitzer Space Telescope has recorded infrared images that reveal a tornado-like shock from a jet of material. The energetic cosmic jet is ploughing through clouds of interstellar gas and impacting into the surrounding matter at almost 160 kilometres per second (100 miles per second). The jet on view is light-years in length, with an intriguing corkscrew-type shape. One possibility is that the jet is threaded along its length by a spiralling magnetic field that originates from the surface and disk of the young star.

One of the advantages of long-lived observatories such as the Hubble Space Telescope is that it is possible to collect repeated images of the same target, thus building up a type of time-lapse movie of any changes. Exposures taken over five or so years can help to trace how the shock waves from the jets of young stellar objects actually move through space. For example, a sequence of Hubble images of the young star XZ Tauri has been secured, residing about 450 light-years away in the constellation of Taurus. Bubbles of glowing gas can be seen billowing away from the star, which is in fact a double star system. The material is ejected into space at almost 150 kilometres per second (93 miles per second), and it extends over 96 billion kilometres (60 billion miles). It seems that the outer edge of the shock wave created by this ejection is decelerating, with speeds dropping from 170 kilometres per second (105 miles per second) to 120 kilometres per second (75 miles per second). These time-lapse images also reveal

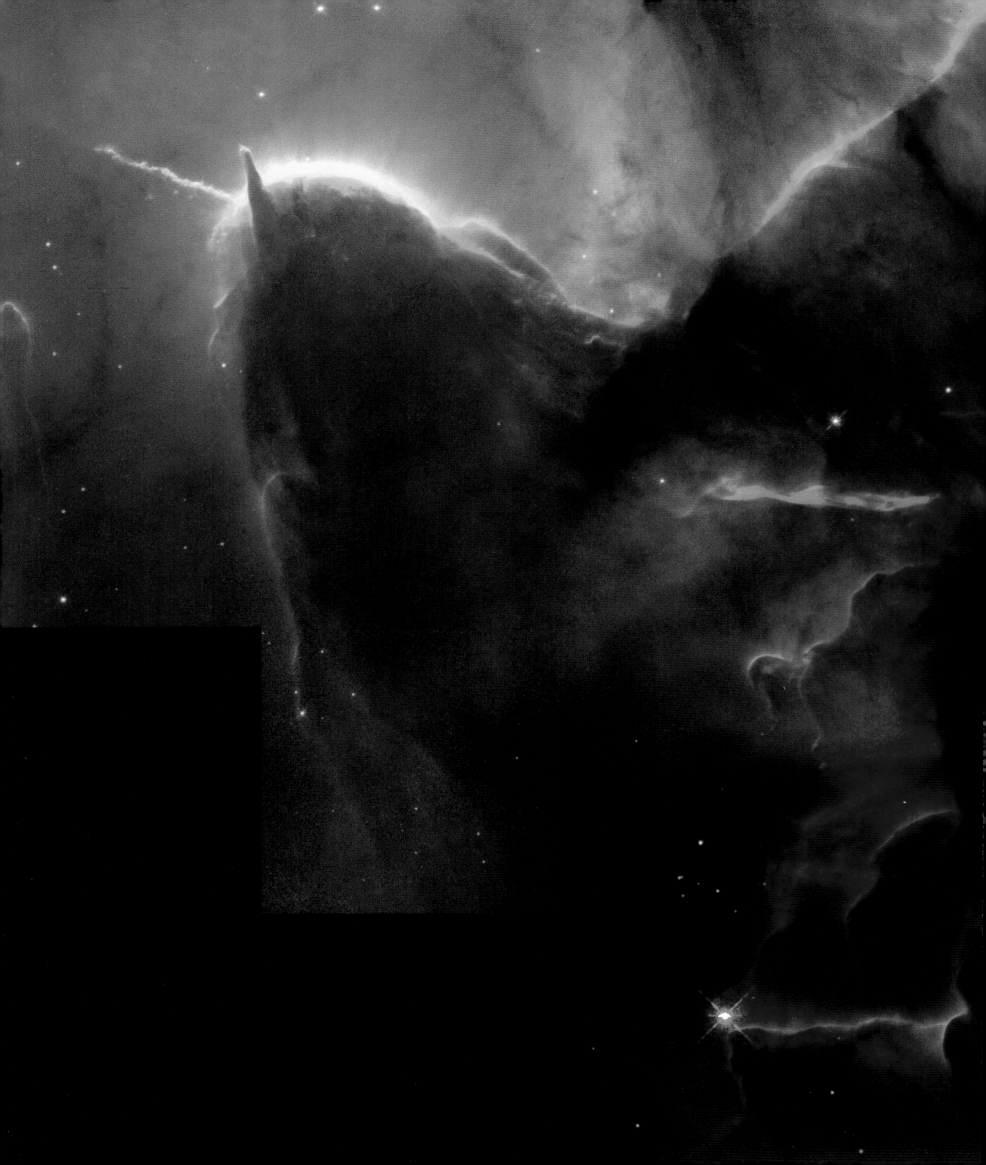

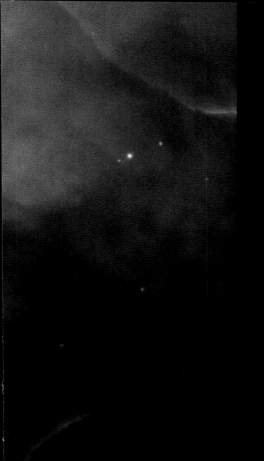

LEFT: *Stellar jets seen protrouding from the tops of dense star-making clouds in the Trifid nebula.*

dramatic changes in the structure of the ejected bubbles of gas as they expand away from the star.

Sometimes a newborn star remains unseen, hiding within a dusty interstellar cloud, but the effects of its dramatic jets can be discerned. A stunning example of such a phenomenon is the object known as Herbig–Haro 2, found in a star-forming region of the vast Orion Nebula. The star itself is not detectable in visible images taken by the Hubble Space Telescope, but clouds of glowing gas are evident about 0.5 light-years away from where a stellar source is noted in infrared and radio telescopes. The shock waves generated by the high-speed jets from the young star heat the gas of the surrounding interstellar clouds, which are then seen radiating visible light in the Hubble images.

The collision between the gas ejected from the young star and the interstellar matter creates sufficient heat to also produce X-rays, which have been detected by observations with NASA's Chandra Telescope. The data suggest that Herbig–Haro 2 contains gas that has been heated by shocks to a temperature of up to a million degrees Celsius (1.8 million degrees Fahrenheit).

Another eerie case where the embryonic star is deeply embedded in a dusty cocoon can be found in the striking Trifid Nebula, almost 9,000 light-years distant in the constellation of Sagittarius. There, a wispy stellar jet is seen emerging from the edges of a dark molecular cloud, within which lies buried the new star itself. Particularly rare is the fact that almost the entire jet is visible, as it glows due to the radiation from other massive stars forming near the centre of the Trifid Nebula. The jet reveals a clumpy shape, somewhat like travelling blobs of matter.

The spacing between the blobs in a jet such as this provides insights into the conditions very close to the star where the jet originates. For example, the flow of material lifted away from the disk around the star is apparently not smooth and continuous, but rather more erratic and bullet-like. The clumpiness of the jet gives an indirect indication that the disk itself may have irregularities and gaps, which in turn may indicate that planets are being formed.

The intense blasts of hot gas streaming away represent a relatively short phase in the early lives of stars, perhaps lasting less than 100,000 years. During this period, the jets can carry away vast amounts of material that might have fallen toward the star. Ultimately, the out-flowing streams of gas help to clear away all the remaining material that surrounds a young star, leaving behind not only a blazing central object, but most likely a system of planets as well.

Building the Milky Way

In order to probe the origins of much larger structures, such as the galaxies, knowledge of how stars form is today being combined with an attempt to understand their histories. For example, astronomers are now seeking to understand the formation of our Milky Way Galaxy, an exercise much like that of archaeologists mining through vast amounts of historical data. Such attempts have been made possible by technological advances that have greatly increased the observational data that can be gathered at the telescopes. It is now possible to embark on surveys that provide rich and detailed data on hundreds of thousands of stars in the Galaxy, and to simultaneously obtain spectrograms that reveal information about stellar ages, chemical composition, motion and location. By analyzing the light output from numerous stars, it is possible to essentially witness the entire 'fossil record' of our Milky Way Galaxy.

At the present time, billions of years after the Milky Way Galaxy first started to assemble, the stars within it are mostly located in an almost spherical central bulge, and along spiral arms that form part of a very thin disk. A much lower spread of stars is also found in a vast spherical halo that envelops the entire disk of the Galaxy, with a diameter of almost 200,000 light-years.

Star formation continues to occur today in the disk of the Galaxy, with numerous stars younger than 100 million years old. (These stars are young when compared to the billions-of-years-old stars that reside in the halo of the Galaxy.) The disk stars, which include the Sun, travel in well-determined, near-circular orbits around the centre of the Galaxy. In contrast, the stars in the Galaxy's halo formed well before an ordered Galaxy had been assembled, so their orbits are more chaotic and eccentric. Indeed, the halo stars occasionally pass through the disk, including some very dim dwarf stars that are thought to be the oldest building blocks of our Galaxy. It is ironic, perhaps, that the most primitive stars we know about have not been discovered in some distant galaxy in the early Universe, but rather in the halo of our own Galaxy.

The history of our Galaxy is made considerably more complex by evidence that it has undergone merges and collisions with other smaller galaxies. The 'fossil' evidence gathered from large surveys of stars provides clues that many stars in our Galaxy may be non-natives, and have been gobbled up during giant galactic collisions. The absorbed dwarf galaxies are today reduced to streams of stars, and their orbits around the centre of the Galaxy are being studied to reveal the manner in which they entered.

Understanding the formation history of our Galaxy will ultimately allow astronomers to tackle the much wider problem of galaxy and star formation in the Universe. To learn about how the Universe has evolved, it is necessary to understand the history of stars. The rate at which stars are made can be quite different between very massive galaxies and low mass ones. By extending their probing surveys to sample hundreds of thousands of galaxies, each loaded with many billions of stars, astronomers hope to unravel the complete star formation history of the Universe.

RIGHT: *Edge-on view of the spiral-shaped galaxy NGC5866 from the Hubble Telescope, revealing contrasting lanes of interstellar dust bordered by newly formed bright blue stars.*

Clustered
Siblings

We have seen in *Reservoirs in Space* (*see page 29*) that most stars are not born in isolation, but form instead as groups from the same nursery in a giant molecular cloud. The vast collapsing cloud may have embedded within it thousands of dark nebulae that ultimately give rise to an incredible number of stars that are close together in space, and which appear within a fairly short period of time. The group of gravitationally bound young stars that is the result of this collective star birth is known as an 'open star cluster'.

Open star clusters are very important to astronomers studying the stars because they provide them with a virtual cosmic laboratory for studying the formation and evolution of stars. The clusters are of great interest because, having formed together, the stars are approximately the same age. Furthermore, since they are born out of the same molecular cloud, the chemical make-up of the stars in a cluster is also very similar. The stars that make up a young, open cluster can, however, have different masses at birth, and this means that they may follow different life paths. We will see in the following chapters that the mass by which a star is born is pivotal in determining how fast it evolves and which stages it goes through, right up to its ultimate demise. The constituents in an open cluster are thus ideally suited for studying how stars of different birth masses evolve. The young star clusters are also superb tools for tracing the history of the Milky Way Galaxy as a whole, and for advancing our knowledge of the structure and motions within its magnificent spiral arms.

Open and Globular Clusters

More than 1,100 open clusters have been discovered in our Milky Way Galaxy, and astronomers estimate that there are a further 100,000 hidden away behind obscuring clouds of gas and dust. Individual open clusters may contain between 100 to 10,000 stars, all of which formed at almost the same time. The younger clusters are distinguished by the strong light output of very hot, bright blue stars.

Open clusters do not remain a group forever, however. Since the clusters reside in the spiral-arm structures of our Galaxy, they are rotated around as a ragged group of stars. During these orbits around the centre of our Galaxy, a cluster may encounter disruptive gravitational forces due to encounters with other collections of stars, or with passing giant clouds of interstellar gas. Over a period of several hundred million years the open cluster will 'evaporate' as its members are gradually dispersed by galactic tidal waves. The cluster stars trail across the Galaxy to become widely spaced field stars, apparently no longer associated with any siblings. Our Sun likely formed as a member of an open cluster that has entirely dispersed over the past few billion years.

The young stars in an open star cluster should not be confused with another grouping of stars known as a globular cluster. Found in the more remote halos of galaxies, the globular clusters are considerably larger than open clusters, and contain between 10,000 to a million stars, bound together by their mutual gravity. Unlike open clusters, the globulars are spherically arranged and contain the oldest (not youngest) stars in a galaxy. Globular clusters are thought to have formed in the earliest stages in the assembly of a galaxy like ours, though their precise origin is still debated. The globular clusters are immense and can be 100 to 200 light-years in diameter, compared to the average span of about five to twenty light-years for a young open cluster.

One of the most conspicuous open star clusters visible in the night sky is the Pleiades cluster. The brightest

RIGHT: *Spitzer Telescope infrared image of the Serpens South open star cluster of about 50 stars, located almost 850 light-years from Earth.*

LEFT: *The globular cluster NGC2808 is one of the most massive known in our Galaxy, containing more than one million stars.*

members of this cluster mark out the 'seven sisters' grouping near the shoulder of the 'bull' in the constellation of Taurus. The Pleiades has a prominent role in ancient mythology and is cited by the Ancient Greeks, including Hesiod in around 700 BC and Homer in around 750 BC. Under very dark and clear skies, the naked eye can pick out almost a dozen stars in the Pleiades cluster, and modern detectors have revealed a further 500 faint constituents, with a total span of about 30 light-years.

The stars in the Pleiades are thought to have been born together around 100 million years ago, and they lie nearly 440 light-years from Earth. The youngest hot stars are surrounded by a blue 'haze', the result of a reflection nebula produced by the dust clouds in the vicinity that reflect the light of the blue stars. The nebula exhibits a wispy structure arising from the tiny light-reflecting dust particles that are lined up by magnetic fields that run through interstellar space.

The Pleiades cluster includes several candidates of exotic stellar types known as 'brown dwarfs'. These objects have masses that are intermediate between that of a giant gas planet, like Jupiter, and a small star. Observations taken in the infrared waveband can help to reveal the brown dwarf stars, together with properties of the dust that reflect blue starlight to produce the blue tint of the nebulae. The Pleiades can also be revealing at other wavebands, such as the radio region where double stars are noted, or ultraviolet emission from the hottest young stars, and even X-rays coming from low-mass stars.

The Magellanic Clouds

We noted earlier that a prodigious site for the birth of new stars is the Small Magellanic Cloud, a small neighbouring galaxy to the Milky Way. This irregular-shaped galaxy is a jewel of the southern sky, located 210,000 light-years away in the constellation of Tucana. The study of stars in the Small Magellanic Cloud is particularly interesting, as the galaxy has a different chemical make up to our Galaxy; in particular it has a lower percentage of heavier elements such as carbon, nitrogen and oxygen.

Out of the several star clusters found in the Small Magellanic Cloud, the most dynamic is the brilliant cluster

embedded in the central regions of a nebula called NGC346. This active open cluster is barely three million years old, and is thought to be a stellar nursery similar to those predicted in the earliest epochs of the Universe. The clouds of gas and dust surrounding the cluster in NGC346 are intricately sculpted, with arched and ragged filaments surrounded by a distinct dusty ridge. Sharp images taken using the Advanced Camera for Surveys

ABOVE: *An infrared composite image showing the main disk and central bulge of our Milky Way Galaxy, together with our neighbouring smaller galaxies, the Large and Small Magellanic clouds (lower right).*

onboard the Hubble Space Telescope indicate that the nebula contains more than 2,500 young stars, including hundreds of very low-mass stars that have not yet settled into a stable phase of nuclear fusion to generate their internal energy. There are, in addition, numerous hot, young, massive stars that provide copious amounts of UV radiation to warm the surrounding gas.

Another spectacular location for current star formation, and a powerful star cluster, can be found in the Large Magellanic Cloud, which is also a satellite galaxy of the Milky Way. Of particular interest is the 30 Doradus nebula, residing 170,000 light-years from Earth. The nebula represents a very fertile region for studying the birth of the most massive stars, some perhaps born with 100 times more mass than the Sun. This fierce cluster of stars was formed about two million years ago, and is seen today emitting vast amounts of energy as ultraviolet radiation, together with strong winds of gas.

Material shed by the massive stars travels away at speeds of more than 1,000 kilometres per second (620 miles per second). Ultimately, these winds slam into the surrounding interstellar clouds of cool hydrogen molecules, resulting in compression and increased gas pressures that can ignite a new phase of star formation. The energy of the central cluster in 30 Doradus is thus essentially triggering the birth of a new generation of even younger stars. The cluster of the most massive, luminous stars, known as R136, is barely 8 light-years in diameter compared to the 650 light-year dimension of the surrounding 30 Doradus nebula. R136 contains tens of infant massive stars, and has become an important site for multi-waveband investigations of the process by which the most massive stars in the Universe are born.

RIGHT: *Prolific formation of new stars seen embedded in the nebula NGC346, almost 210,000 light-years away in the Small Magellanic Cloud.*

Starbursts

There are some remarkable settings in space where the conditions are ripe for the formation of hundreds of thousands of very young stars squeezed into a very small volume. Known as superstar clusters, these extreme environments usually signal the consequences of very violent episodes of star formation. The growth of superstar clusters may be triggered, for example, by the collision of two galaxies, or even a close encounter between them. The gravitational forces when galaxies approach each other can be enormous, leading to the unrelenting compression of vast clouds of interstellar gas and dust. The result is to initiate prolific episodes of star formation.

An outstanding example of a superstar cluster currently residing in the Milky Way Galaxy is Westerlund 1. It lies about 10,000 light-years from Earth, in a direction facing toward the centre of our Galaxy. Westerlund 1 contains 100,000 times the mass of the Sun, and includes hundreds of massive stars, each with a luminous output equivalent to a million Suns. Remarkably, this vast collection of powerful stars is compacted within a region that is less than 6 light-years across. This superstar cluster is estimated to be very young, perhaps only between 3.5 and 5 million years old. Its population of very massive stars will evolve relatively quickly, and in less than 50 million years from now, Westerlund 1 is predicted to become a cosmic firework display, with the eruption of thousands of supernovae explosions.

Superstar clusters are generally seen at considerably greater distances than Westerlund 1, and mostly where pairs or groups of galaxies are merging or interacting. The resulting gravitational effect leads to starburst galaxies that host enormous episodes of star formation. The close encounter between galaxies sets up shock waves that speed through and push on giant clouds of interstellar gas. This disturbance causes the clouds to gravitationally collapse, and leads to the birth of massive clusters of stars. The frantic activity may last about ten million years, but this is still a tiny fraction of the several-billion-year age of the galaxies.

Starburst galaxies commonly contain dense clusters of stars with a total mass of millions of Suns, squeezed into only a few light-years in diameter. The rates at which stars form during a starburst can be hundreds of times greater than would have been the case for a normal, solitary galaxy. Furthermore, the star birth can be so violent that it can radically alter the structure of the host galaxy. The new stars generated in a starburst can collectively inject significant amounts of energy and mass into the region of space between

LEFT: *A composite of Spitzer (infrared), Hubble (optical) and Chandra (X-ray) images of the dynamic starburst galaxy M82, located 11.7 million light-years from Earth.*

galaxies via superwinds that create vast expanding bubbles of matter.

NGC1275 is a very unusual and highly luminous galaxy that exhibits starburst activity. Originally discovered by astronomer William Herschel (1738–1822) in 1786, this galaxy is the dominant member of a large group of galaxies known as the Perseus cluster. (This is a cluster of galaxies on an enormous scale in space, as opposed to a cluster of stars within a galaxy.) Even at a distance of about 235 million light-years, incredible details of violent star formation have been revealed in images taken by the Hubble Space Telescope. NGC1275 is also a strong source of radio emission and X-ray radiation.

The active birth of stars is due to an ongoing collision between NGC1275 and a second elliptical shaped galaxy. The result of this merger is seen as vast dust lanes and luminous blue patches that mark regions of substantial star formation. NGC1275 is rich not only in gas and dust, but also in the rise of very compact and massive star clusters, each of which may contain between 100,000 to a million stars. These compact clusters tend to form along the extended filaments of gas that arise from the gravitational interaction of the colliding galaxies.

A further outstanding example of the clustered birth of stars in an interacting galaxy is presented by UGC10214, a peculiar galaxy about 400 million light-years away toward the constellation of Draco. UGC10214 has been distorted due to a galactic collision with a smaller, more compact galaxy. The strong gravitational pull from this interaction has resulted in a long streamer of stars and gas, stretching away for almost 300,000 light-years. Bursts of new star formation are seen in super clusters that appear as bright blue patches in the spiral arms of UGC10214, and also along the streaming debris tail. Each cluster contains up to a million very hot, massive stars that would not have appeared if the two galaxies were widely spaced and in isolation. The clusters in the tidal tail are relatively young – between three and ten million years old – a fact suggesting that they formed close to their present positions.

The consequences of yet another cosmic collision is spectacularly on show around a galaxy called AM0644–741, about 300 million light-years distant. This is the rare case where an immense collision between two galaxies has created stunning ring-like structures around the larger galaxy. The gravitational disruption of the impact created a shock wave that moved somewhat like a ripple across the surface of a pond. The compression of gas and dust caused by the propagating wave has led

to rampant star formation in rings with diameters of 15,000 light-years. These brilliant interlocking rings are hosts to the continuous formation of new stars that are tens of times more massive than the Sun, and considerably hotter. The abundant new stars arise in sparkling blue clusters, where the rate of star birth is three times greater than expected for the main galaxy had there not been a collision. Ring galaxies such as AM0644–741 provide shining examples of how gravitational forces can transform the shape of a galaxy and radically alter the star formation process.

ABOVE: *Exquisite details revealed by Hubble images of the colliding galaxy NGC1275, including dust lanes and bright blue regions of active starbirth.*

RIGHT: *The Tadpole Galaxy (UGC 10214) has been distorted by a merger with another galaxy, resulting in a long streamer which includes dense knots of star-forming clouds.*

RIGHT: *A bright ring of new star clusters is seen in this Hubble Telescope image of a galaxy called AM0644-741, located 300 million light-years away.*

The First Generation of Stars

The birth of stars did not take place immediately after the Universe began 13.7 billion years ago. Current predictions of the theories of cosmology hold that during its first few hundred million years, the Universe contained clouds of gas and dark matter, but no stars. It took several hundred million years after the 'Big Bang' origin of the Universe, before the cosmic 'dark ages' were finally ended, and the first generation of stars ignited. Astronomers are today seeking to understand how this critical transition from darkness to light came about, and how the original collection of elementary atomic particles coalesced over time to form the very first stars.

When we look back at objects formed in the earliest epochs of the Universe, we are looking at structures so distant from us that the light emitting from them takes thousands of millions of years to travel through space and reach our telescopes on Earth. Whilst large, powerful telescopes have allowed astronomers to observe infant galaxies that were assembled as early as 850 million years after the Big Bang, it is currently thought that the first observable stars are likely to have formed barely 300 million years after the Big Bang.

The period between about one million and one billion years after the beginning of the Universe is essentially unobserved, and spans the time when stars and galaxies begin to form. The next generation of telescopes, including the 6.5-metre-diameter follow-up to the Hubble Space Telescope known as the James Webb Space Telescope, will permit us to probe more directly into this enigmatic period, when stars were being made from pristine material.

The study of the first stars born in the Universe is therefore currently not conducted by their direct observation. Rather, astronomers rely on theories of cosmology and simulations carried out on powerful computers to examine the process. The star-making conditions in the infant Universe would have been very different to those that we witness in our Milky Way and other local galaxies. The first generation of stars in the Universe would have formed in the absence of dust, cosmic rays and strong magnetic fields. When the Universe first formed, the only elements available for making stars were mostly hydrogen and some helium. (We will see in *The Evolution and Demise of Stars*, page 136, that elements such as oxygen, carbon and iron can only be forged by nuclear fusion in the cores of stars.) The first generation of stars must therefore have formed using the primordial hydrogen and helium only.

It is predicted that the first stars to form in the Universe were very massive at birth, with perhaps more than 100 times the mass of the Sun. These stars would have fragmented out of clouds of primarily hydrogen gas, and with the onset of nuclear fusion, would have released enormous amounts of radiation. These hefty stars evolved very rapidly toward catastrophically powerful demises, likely as scaled-up supernovae explosions.

It is thought that the scale of formation of stars in the Universe peaked about five billion years ago, and the rate of birth has declined dramatically since then. Today, old stars are dying much faster than new stars are being formed, which will eventually lead to a dimming of the Universe. About 100 trillion years after its Big Bang origin, all gas in the Universe will have been consumed into stars, and the formation of new stars will come to an end.

RIGHT: *Hundreds of galaxies revealed in a deep Hubble Telescope image, including several cases of galaxies distorted due to mergers and collisions.*

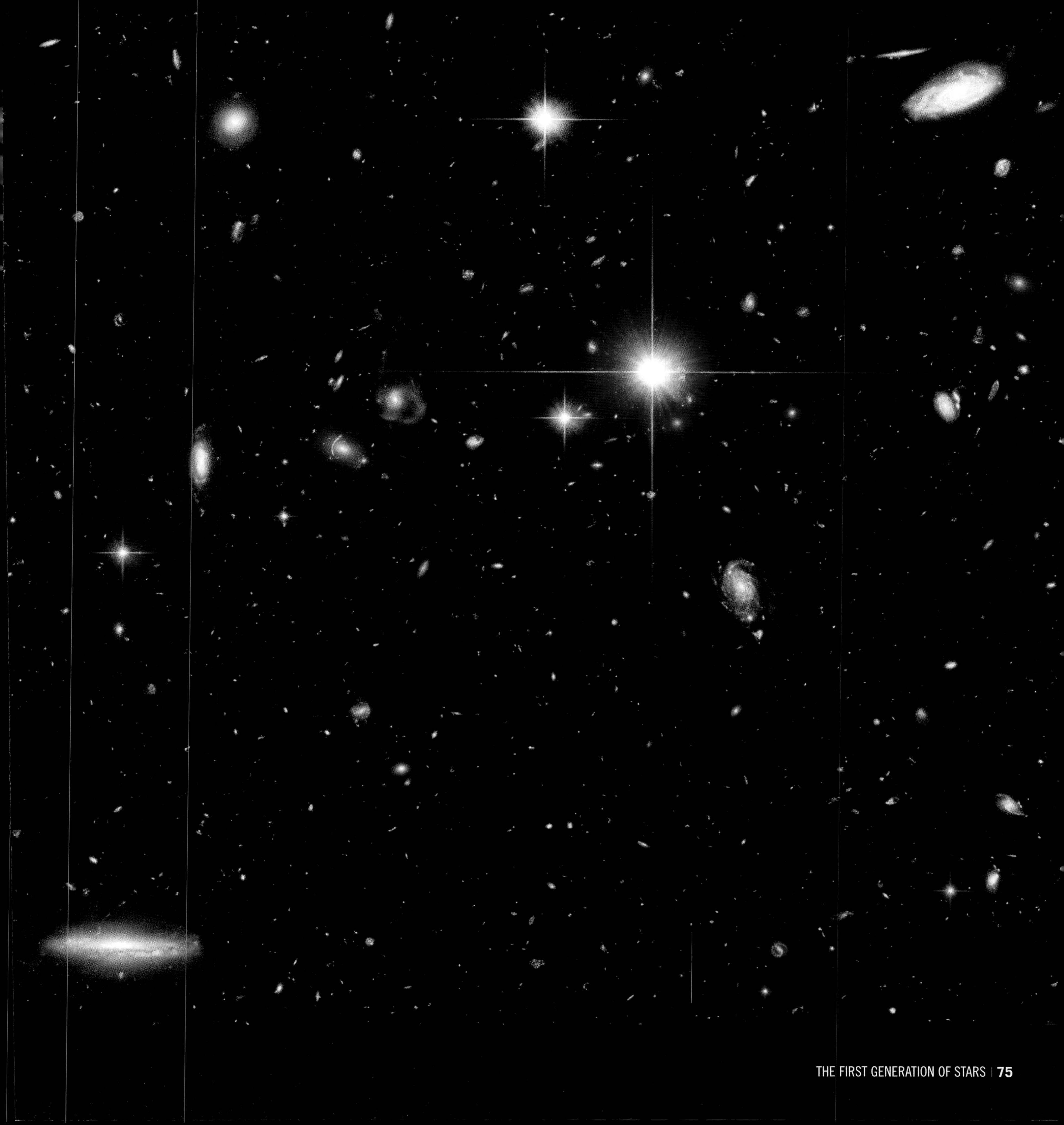

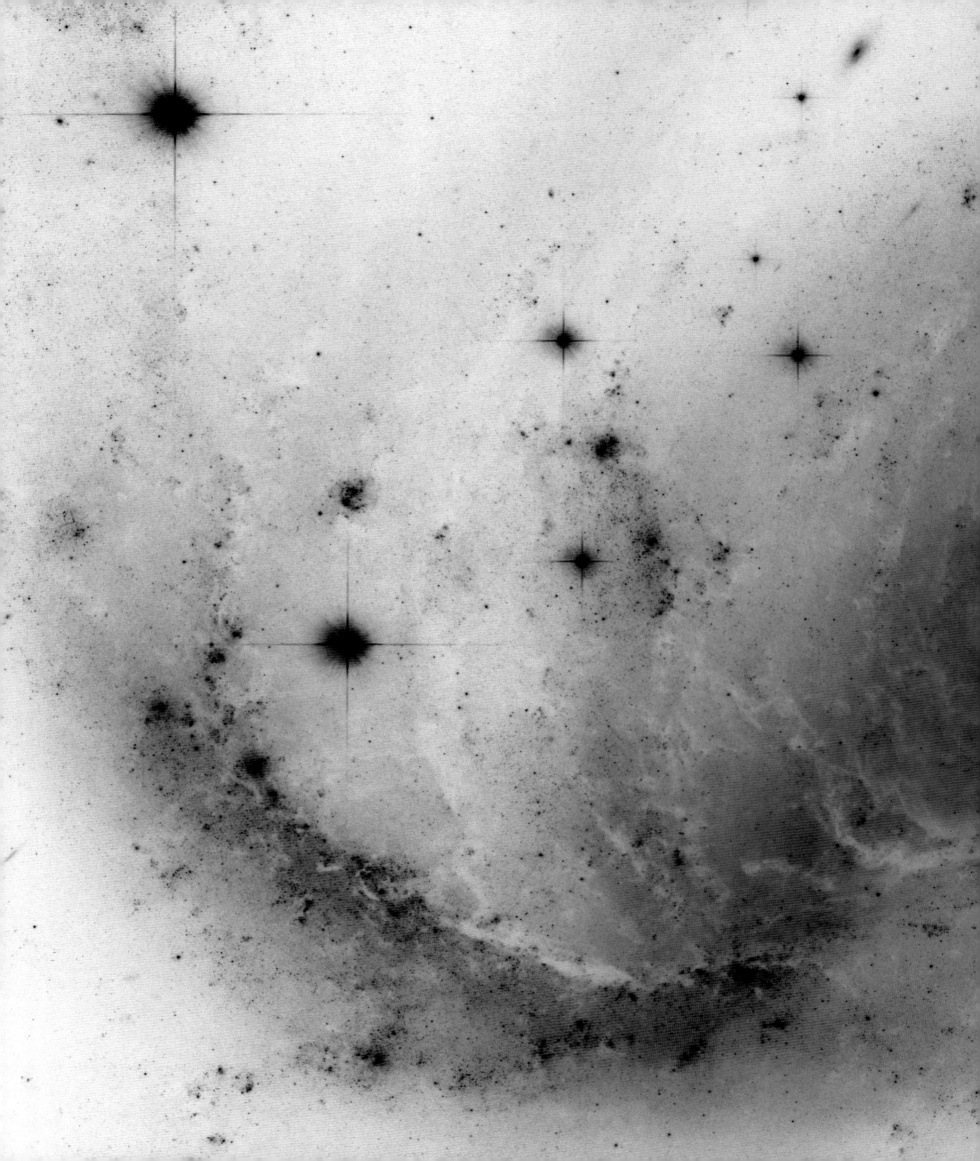

Part two

GLORIOUS LIFE

The Stellar Zoo

There is a rich variety of star types in our Galaxy. This fundamental observation becomes quickly apparent to anyone gazing up at a clear night sky with dark-adapted eyes, well away from the glare of city lights. Looking carefully at the sky, three observational properties are immediately discernable. Firstly, the stars are not all equally bright; some appear dimmer than others. Secondly, the stars are not all the same colour, exhibiting instead a mixture of subtle shades. For example, Aldebaran, in the constellation of Taurus, is reddish, and the bright cluster of stars in the Pleiades is blue. Lastly, a glance at the night sky will show that the stars are not evenly scattered. Indeed, their uneven distribution has in part provided the basis for ancient astronomers to visualize shapes in the sky, and to link these shapes to the myths and legends associated with the constellations' names.

The thousands of stars visible to our naked eyes and the billions of stars that make up the Milky Way Galaxy have a range of physical properties: they have different surface temperatures; they differ in size; and they lie at various distances from the Earth. The diverse stellar zoo is made up of bright, hot stars that live for a relatively short time, and cool, dim stars that last for a very long time. Some stars are massive, with powerful winds blowing away from their surfaces; others are paired so that they co-exist in tight orbits around each other. There are stars that have only recently emerged from a nursery of gas, while others are cooling cinders of dying objects. Indeed, a list of more than 180 different types of star categories can be compiled from a search through scientific literature. The fundamental reason why so many different star types are on view is that our current 'snapshot' of the galaxy contains stars that are at different stages in their life cycles.

LEFT: *Hundreds of thousands of stars are seen in this infrared view toward the central region of our Milky Way Galaxy.*

Analysing Starlight

Astronomers determine many key details about stars by studying the light they emit. We have noted, for instance, that many of the stars in the night sky are different colours. The reason for this variation is simply that a star's colour is related to how hot it is. An iron poker heated in a fire provides a simple analogue: The poker will glow and become red hot, and raising its temperature further will make it white-hot, and eventually bluish-white. Similarly, the temperature in the surface layer of the Sun is about 5,800 degrees Celsius (10,500 degrees Fahrenheit), making it radiate a yellow-white colour. The giant star known as Antares, in the constellation of Scorpius, has a surface temperature of just 3,000 degrees Celsius (5,400 degrees Fahrenheit), and hence it shines with a reddish hue. In contrast, the blue star known as Rigel has a surface temperature of almost 10,000 degrees Celsius (18,000 degrees Fahrenheit). Most stars look white to the human eye only because they are too faint to activate the eye's colour receptors.

Even the most casual glance at the night sky reveals that the stars have different degrees of brightness. Astronomers refer to this diversity as a range of apparent stellar magnitudes. There are two basic reasons for this spread in brightness. Firstly, the stars are not all the same distance from us. Stars that have a lower power output can appear bright to us simply because they may be closer to us. The Sun, which is in fact a very ordinary star, is an extreme example of this. Imagine the way a torch held in your hand would appear brighter than a distant streetlight even though the torch is, in absolute comparison, much fainter. A star might also appear brighter because it is intrinsically more powerful, and is emitting a greater rate of energy. These stars are more luminous and, in most cases, are also a lot bigger, with greater surface areas.

To derive quantitative information about objects in space, astronomers use a special instrument called a spectrograph to split the starlight into its constituent colours. The result of this 'splitting up of the light' is recorded as a spectrum. A familiar natural spectrum occurs when light from the Sun bounces around inside millions of raindrops, aligning itself into its various colours to form a rainbow. Following on from the discoveries of Sir Isaac Newton (1642–1727) in the mid-17th century, scientists working in laboratories can disperse light into a spectrum using a glass prism. Modern astronomical observatories are equipped with complex spectrographs that use gratings instead of glass to yield very detailed and high-precision spectra. Indeed, astronomers employ large, powerful telescopes on Earth or in space mostly for the purpose of collecting light that is then passed through a spectrograph, as opposed to taking direct images of objects.

Today, the spectrograph has become the most powerful tool of astronomical research. The analyses of spectra can provide information about the temperature, chemical composition, density, motion and other parameters of a star, galaxy or planet. However, decoding and understanding the spectra of stars requires detailed knowledge of the way atoms and molecules can emit and absorb light. Much of this knowledge is derived from the work carried out during the early part of the 20th century by leading physicists such as Maxwell Planck (1858–1947), Niels Bohr (1885–1962) and Ernest Rutherford (1871–1937).

RIGHT: *Hot blue stars are seen nestled within giant star-forming clouds in this Hubble Space Telescope view toward the Carina spiral arm of the Milky Way Galaxy.*

Stellar Fingerprints

When light passes through the uppermost layers of a star, atoms in the gas can absorb certain specific wavelengths of the light, thus producing a spectrum that is a continuous spread of colours, but which is broken up by dark, narrow bands. The pattern of these bands, known as absorption lines, is unique for each type of chemical element that makes up the gas cloud. For each type of atom, theories of atomic physics can predict the precise position and intensity of these bands, which are, in fact, mostly determined by the temperature and composition of the star.

Since different stars may have different chemical make-ups, we can tell them apart by examining their stellar spectra. The spectrum of a star is thus like a stellar fingerprint: it can be used to differentiate between objects in space, and it can also tell us what groups of stars have in common.

Astronomers use the spectra of stars to classify them into different types, and to understand their physical properties. Indeed, a star's spectrum is the best tool we have for studying its light. Stellar spectra were first recorded in the early 1800s, when stars with very similar spectra were classified together. In the 1860s, a Jesuit priest based in Rome named Father Angelo Secchi (1818–1878) made the first serious attempts to classify the stars according to the spectral lines they exhibited. These attempts were followed by the work of astronomers such as Edward Charles Pickering (1846–1919) and Williamina Fleming (1857–1911) at the Harvard College Observatory, in the United States, who classified more than 10,000 stars using letters of the alphabet to denote the strengths of the absorption lines due to hydrogen.

During the late 19th and early 20th centuries, Annie Cannon (1863–1941), also at Harvard, significantly extended the work of Pickering and Fleming to catalogue and classify the spectra of almost 225,000 stars. This

BELOW: *The spectrum of the Sun, with numerous dark bands or spectral lines due to a variety of chemical elements.*

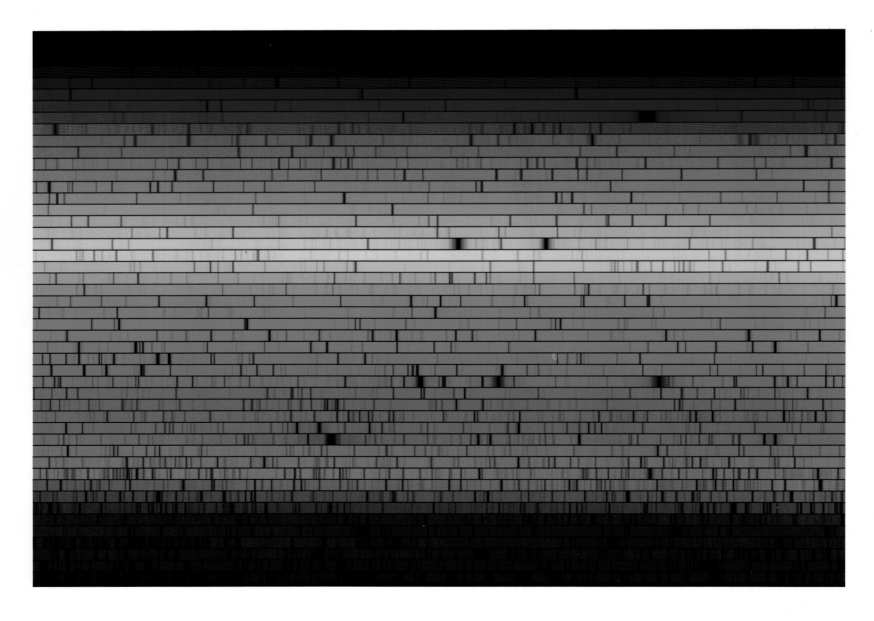

remarkable effort led to the formally adopted spectral classification scheme of stars that is still in use today. The challenge faced by astronomers such as Annie Cannon was analogous to that tackled earlier in the biological sciences with the classification of living organisms. Annie Cannon arranged the spectra of stars to represent decreasing temperature in their outer layers, resulting in a letter sequence that ran **O, B, A, F, G, K, M**. The arrangement goes from hotter to cooler objects. She also further divided most of the letters using numbers ranging from 0 to 9. For example, according to her classification system, an O star is much hotter than an M star, and a B3 star is hotter than a B9 star. (Our Sun is a G2 star within this classification scheme.) The hottest O-type stars have temperatures in the range 28,000 to 50,000 degrees Celsius (50,000 to 90,000 degrees Fahrenheit), while M-type stars are rather cool objects of between 2,500 to 3,500 degrees Celsius (4,500 to 6,300 degrees Fahrenheit).

The development of more powerful and larger telescopes during the late 20th century has led to the discovery of further stellar types. New 'L-' and 'T-type' designations are used today to classify objects that are even fainter and

ABOVE: *The 200,000 light-year distant open star cluster NGC290, which exhibits a rich variety of stellar types.*

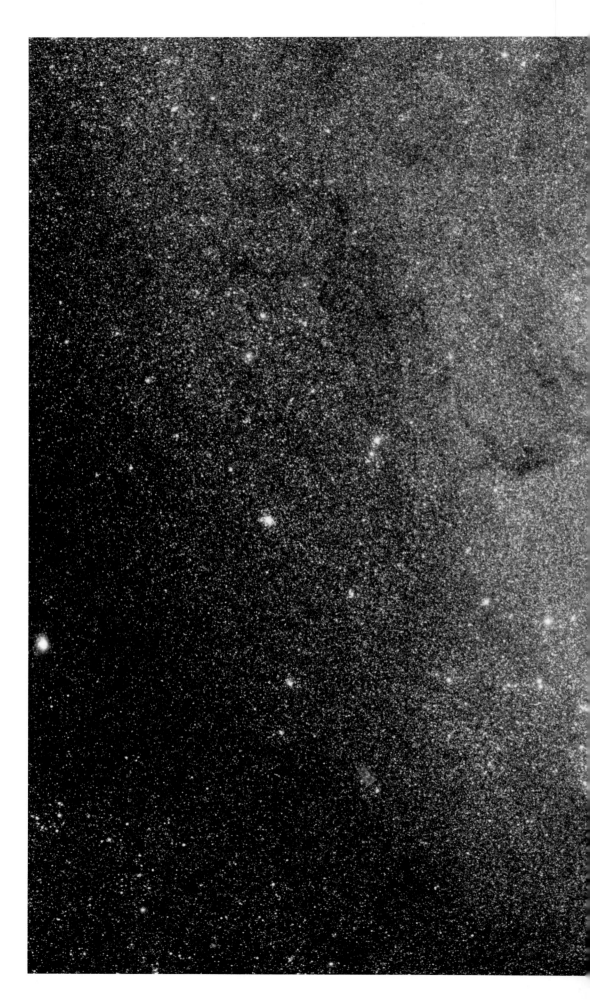

RIGHT: *The tremendous variety of stars present in the central regions of the spiral-shaped galaxy NGC300, about 6.5 million light-years away.*

cooler than M-type stars. There are also C-type stars, which exhibit spectra that are unusually rich in the element carbon, and usually show a deep-red colour when viewed through a telescope. Particularly rare are S-type stars, whose spectra show chemically exotic bands due to zirconium oxide and lanthanum oxide.

There was a significant complication in the early attempts to classify the spectra of stars. It turns out that many stars of the same spectral type, such as a group of A3 stars or K5 stars, did not necessarily have identical spectral lines. Although the patterns and strengths of the absorption lines were often similar, the width of the dark bands evident in the spectra somehow differed. For example, in a pair of F7 stars, one might have narrow, sharp absorption lines, while the other may exhibit much broader lines. Astronomers soon realized this variation in width was due to differences in the atmospheric pressure in the upper layers of the stars. The pressure, in turn, represented the surface gravity of the star, and thus its size. It became apparent that some stars are immense and bloated, while others are compact; both can, however, have the same surface temperature.

The essential difference amongst the stars is their total power output, or luminosity. Imagine, for example, the way in which a huge flame from a one-metre-tall candle would provide more heat energy than a 10-centimetre candle, even though both are made from the same material and both are burning at identical temperatures. The larger candle is more luminous simply because its larger flame has a greater surface area. The constituents of our Galaxy include dwarf stars such as the Sun; giant stars like Mira, which is tens of times larger than the Sun; and supergiant stars that have radii hundreds of times greater than the Sun. To illustrate the vastness of the radii of these supergiant stars, if the supergiant star Betelgeuse, in the constellation of Orion, was placed at the centre of our solar system, its surface layer would extend out to the orbit of Mars.

The most massive stars in our Galaxy are remarkably luminous, and can shine with the equivalent output of a million Suns. These stars can have surface temperatures of up to 50,000 degrees Celsius (90,000 degrees Fahrenheit), and are known as 'blue supergiants'. Zeta Puppis, the brightest star in the southern constellation of Puppis, is a prominent blue supergiant. These powerful, massive stars have relatively short and unstable lives, but

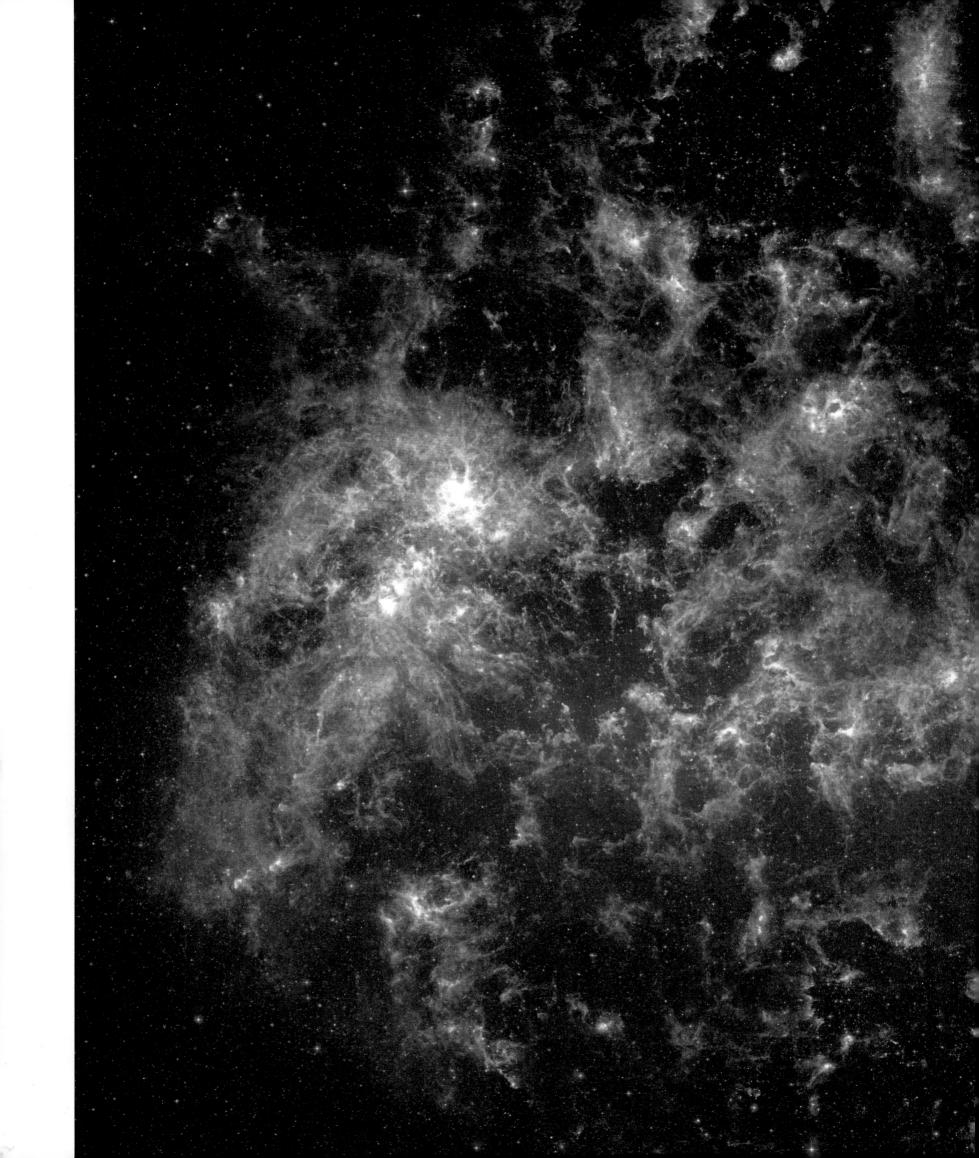

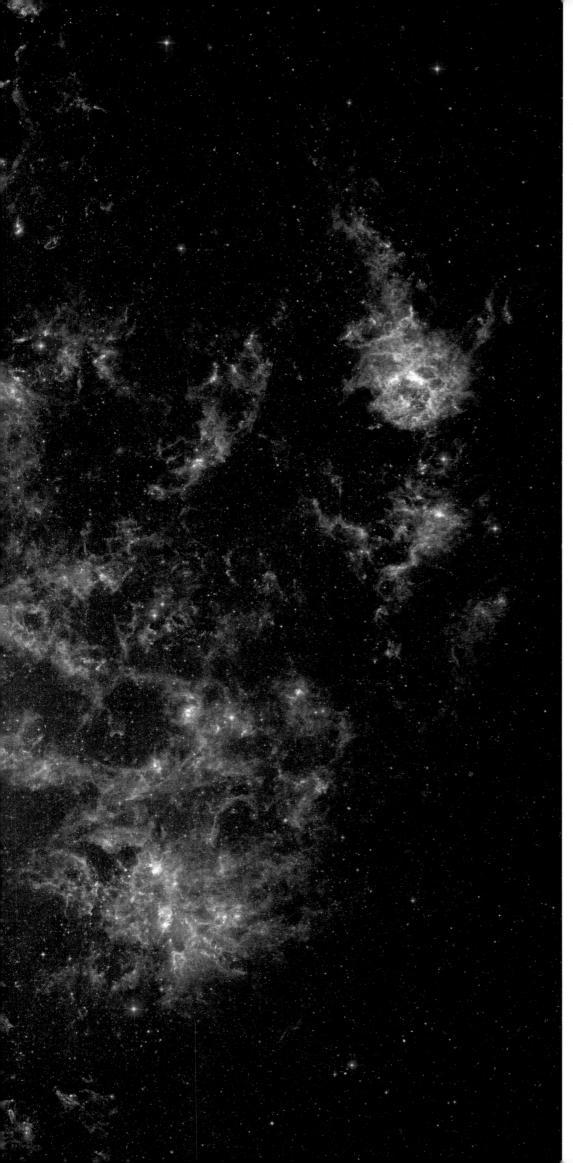

since they are amongst the brightest stars in the Universe, they can be picked out and studied not only in our Galaxy, but also in other galaxies millions of light-years away.

Through the power of spectroscopy, the light from the many thousands of stars we see as point-like objects in the sky can be analysed to derive information about their sizes and temperatures. We can now appreciate that the rich variety of stars we see on a clear night is due to the fact that some are cooler than others; some have ballooned into vast supergiants; and others are compact and dim.

The reason for the wide variety of stellar types is that every individual star has a life history, and evolves over billions of years. Imagine, for example, that an alien being visited Earth and had just one day to observe human beings and to understand how they age. Twenty-four hours is, of course, too short a time to actually see someone age. The best approach would be for the alien to visit a single town and to study its newborn babies, young children in schools, teenagers and adults in a family, elderly people in a park, and perhaps someone dying. At the end of its one-day visit, the alien might collate its observations and deduce that the baby must grow in order to become a teenager, then to turn into an adult, and eventually to reach retirement age. In much the same way, the life of an astronomer is far too short to witness the full evolution of a star. Snapshot observations are used instead to study star-forming clouds; dwarf stars such as the Sun; red giant stars; supergiant stars; perhaps even a star exploding as a supernova. Only with some clever detective work is it possible to understand the life stories of stars; for example, to know that the dwarf star will, sometime in the future, swell into a giant or supergiant and will ultimately either explode as a violent supernova, or die more sedately as its outer layers are puffed out into space.

LEFT: *Infrared view of a variety of young and old stars, together with hot and cold dust, in our neighbouring galaxy – the Large Magellanic Cloud.*

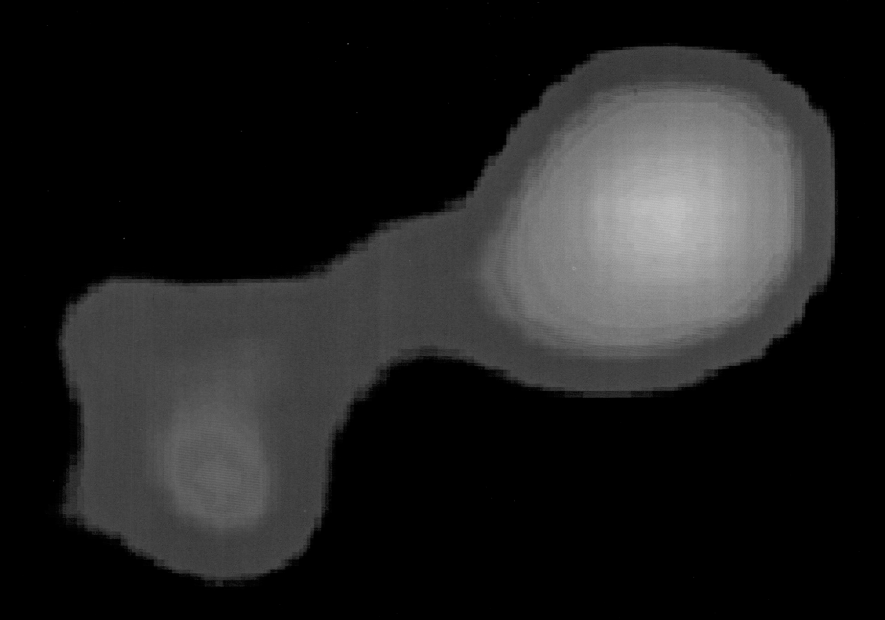

Living in Pairs

The Sun is exceptional in that it appears as an isolated star in space. More than half of the objects we see as single stars in the night sky with unaided eyes are actually pairs of stars that orbit around each other. A pair of co-orbiting stars is known as a 'binary star'. The study of binary stars is very important in astronomy, as analysis of their starlight can reveal critical information on the masses, sizes and outer layers of the stars. The two components in a binary star system may be separated by a fraction of a light-year, or they could be almost touching and thus highly interacting. An intriguing aspect of binary stars is that very different objects can be paired, including low- and high-mass stars, very compact dwarfs and bloated supergiants, and red and blue stars. A striking example of a double star with contrasting red and blue colours is Albireo, near the 'neck'

of the constellation of Cygnus, the swan. Albirio is referred to as a 'visual binary', and telescope observations can easily reveal that the two stars orbit around each other. Another well-studied visual binary system is Castor, in the constellation of Gemini. In a visual binary, wide distances separate the stars, and the orbital periods are usually long, perhaps as long as hundreds of years.

Binary or multiple star systems can become bound by gravity in two primary ways. We have already seen that the original parent nebula, made of gas and dust, will fragment as it collapses to yield numerous dense clumps. Some of these clumps may give rise to two constituent stars that form close to each other, and become gravitationally tied to make a binary system. Another possible scenario for the formation of a stellar pair could occur if a single star were to approach a more massive star too closely; the former could get locked into orbit by the gravitational pull of the latter. This scenario may occur in situations involving

compact clusters that contain thousands of stars, making the prospect of gravitational interactions more likely.

Sometimes the stellar components in a co-orbiting system are too close to each other and cannot be resolved visually, even through a telescope. In these cases it is possible to unravel the binary nature of the system by passing the starlight through a spectrograph. The resultant spectrum can reveal the orbital motion of the stars through regular or cyclic shifts in the absorption lines (or bands). This is known as the Doppler effect, which distorts the light waves arriving from the stars depending on their direction of motion. Known as spectroscopic binaries, more than 1,500 systems have been detected using this method. Since the stars in a spectroscopic binary orbit much closer together than in a visual binary, the former have much shorter orbital periods. Also in the constellation of Cygnus, Algol is a spectroscopic binary where the stars orbit each other about once every two days and 20 hours.

Occasionally, a pairs of stars can come extremely close together, resulting in powerful and extraordinary effects. If we had X-ray eyes, the night sky would appear extremely different, as our view would be dominated by a few very bright sources that emit copious amounts of X-ray radiation. The brightest of these sources are called X-ray binaries. X-ray binaries are made up of a normal star (not unlike our Sun) and a highly compressed object such as a neutron star, or a black hole. (We will see in the final chapter that these compact objects are exotic end-states left over after the evolution of massive stars.) The pair of stars is so close together that the intense gravity of the neutron star, or the black hole, can strip material off the normal star.

Vast amounts of energy are released during the extreme interaction between such stars. The gas drawn away from the normal star enters into orbit around the compressed star, forming a swirling disk of hot material. The disk contains in-falling gas that may be heated to one million

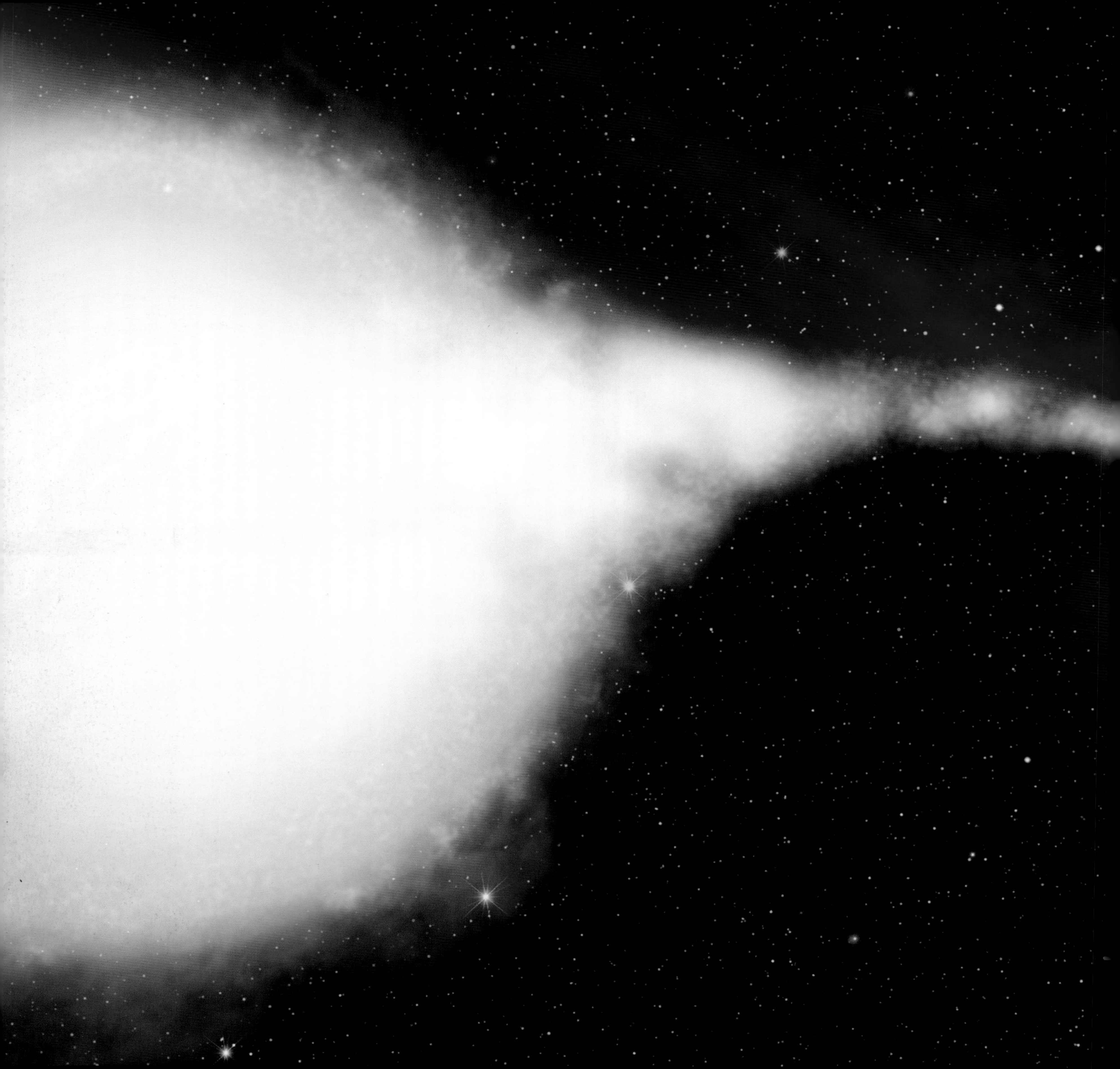

degrees Celsius (1.8 million degrees Fahrenheit), and this energy is predominantly radiated in the X-rays. The remarkable X-ray binary system allows astronomers to probe extreme conditions that cannot be reproduced on Earth.

A well-studied example of an X-ray binary is Cygnus X-1, located thousands of light-years away toward the centre of the constellation of Cygnus. One of the two stars locked together by the mutual gravitational influences is a luminous blue supergiant of about 30 times the mass of the Sun. The other partner in the Cygnus X-1 binary act is far more exotic. It is one of the first suspected black hole candidates, mooted as such following measurements made by the UHURU X-ray satellite in the 1970s. Hot gas spinning in a disk around the black hole is heated to fierce temperatures as the material violently rubs together in a friction-like manner. The strength of the X-rays, together with observations that the radiation flickers over hundredths of a second, provides unique evidence that the object at the centre of the disk in Cygnus X-1 is a black hole.

Among subsequent discoveries is the system V404 Cygni, which presents what is probably the best evidence to date that X-ray binaries can contain black holes with masses of a few times that of the Sun. The 'normal' star in V404 Cygni is a yellow-orange object that is slightly less massive than the Sun, and it orbits its unseen partner once every 6.5 days. This rapid motion means that the two stars must be very close to each other. Detailed studies of the X-rays produced as gas is ripped away from the yellow-orange star, together with careful measurements of how it orbits indicates the presence of a black hole that has a mass of about 12 times that of the Sun.

In the study of X-ray binary systems, astronomers are essentially using X-ray telescopes to detect the effect of the gravity of a black hole on nearby gas. Since light cannot escape from a black hole, the measurements of a visible star orbiting around an invisible object, and the manner in which gas is stripped away from the former, provides the strongest clues that a black hole is present.

LEFT: *Artist's impression of the Cygnus X-1 black hole binary star system, where gas is spiralling away from a massive blue supergiant star*

Exploding Binaries

The subset of the stellar zoo that includes objects paired together by their mutual gravitational pull includes another fascinating example known as a 'nova'. This is an exploding stellar pairing in which the smaller, more compressed star is an Earth-sized body known as a white dwarf. Just as black holes mark the end point in the evolution of massive stars, white dwarfs are the stellar tombstones at the end of the lives of Sun-like stars. In a nova, a normal red giant star donates matter around a white dwarf as the pair orbit closely around each other. The red giant dumps hydrogen gas onto the surface of the white dwarf via a swirling plate-like disk. The extreme gravity of the white dwarf squeezes and heats the hydrogen. If enough material from the disk is heaped onto the white dwarf, the hydrogen gas will get sufficiently hot to ignite nuclear-fusion reactions. The result is a thermonuclear explosion on the surface of the white dwarf, which is the characteristic signature of a nova. The whole spinning disk of matter surrounding the white dwarf can be blown away in the eruption. The red giant star itself is not grossly disturbed, however, and in some cases the whole process of drawing gas onto the compact white dwarf star can start all over again. In some binary stars, therefore, the nova explosion can occur in repeated cycles of many hundreds or even thousands of years apart.

A recent example of a nova explosion occurred on 12 February 2006, when a rapid increase in brightness of a faint star known as RS Ophiuchi could be seen. Located more than 5,000 light-years away from Earth, the red giant and white dwarf binary system had undergone a nova explosion. The event triggered an international campaign of intensive observations using ground-based and space telescopes. This was, in fact, the sixth recorded nova explosion in RS Ophiuchi over a span of 108 years. The effects of the explosion were witnessed not only with optical telescopes, but also in the X-ray, infrared and radio regions of the electromagnetic spectrum. Indeed, RS Ophiuchi had presented a rare opportunity to exploit co-ordinated observations and probing instrumentation in order to study the effects of the nuclear explosion on the white dwarf, and its aftermath on the whole binary system. The initial blast wave from the explosion travelled out at almost 3,500 kilometres per second (2,175 miles per second), and dispersed important heavy chemical elements into space.

Yet another reason why the study of binary stars is so important in stellar astronomy is that these stars offer the most reliable way to study stellar mass. Knowledge of a star's mass is vital for understanding and predicting the evolutionary path the star will follow. By application of Isaac Newton's (1642–1727) laws of gravity, the mass of a star can be determined by the gravitational effect it has on another body. Using telescope observations, astronomers can derive the period of the orbit of a binary star and the distance between the two objects. These two pieces of data can then be combined to derive the stellar mass.

RIGHT: *Hubble Telescope image of the Pismis 24 open-star cluster, which hosts a massive binary star system where each of the two components is 100 times the mass of the Sun.*

Changing Before Our Eyes

Though the stars in the night sky appear to shine in an unchanging manner, some do in fact vary in brightness over short time-scales of days, weeks and months. More than 30,000 variable stars have been catalogued, including many for which the behaviour in brightness follows a very regular and repeating pattern or cycle. Variable stars represent another important class of objects since their change in brightness often reflects a fundamental adjustment in the structure of the star itself. The light output of the star might vary in a cyclic manner over several days because its surface layers are contracting and expanding. These pulsating stars may thus be undergoing changes in their size and temperature. They are likely in a very unstable phase of their lives.

One important group of pulsating objects is known as the Cepheid variables. These are very luminous supergiant stars that change their brightness factor, with regular peaks of between one day and about 60 days. Cepheid variables have received a lot of scientific attention because the manner in which their brightness changes can be interpreted so as to derive a distance to the star. Furthermore, since Cepheid variables are very bright stars, they can be monitored not just across our Milky Way Galaxy, but also millions of light-years away in other galaxies. For this reason, the Cepheid variables are sometimes referred to as 'cosmic distance indicators'. Sharp Hubble Space Telescope images have been used to pick out Cepheid variables in the magnificent spiral-patterned galaxy known as M100. By recording the systematic changes in the brightness of Cepheid stars, astronomers were able to determine that M100 is 56 million light-years from Earth. Cosmic yardsticks such as those provided by Cepheid variable stars are therefore vital in the attempt to ascertain the precise determination of the size and age of the Universe.

LEFT: *Hubble image of spiral galaxy NGC1309, which hosts Cepheid variable stars that have been monitored to help determine a distance to the galaxy of around 100 million light-years.*

ailed Stars

A collapsing cloud of interstellar gas and dust can sometimes lead to the birth of an object that is not massive enough or dense enough to generate energy from the nuclear fusion reactions in its central core. These 'failed stars' are known as 'brown dwarfs'. Astronomers estimate that the population of brown dwarfs within galaxies may equal that of normal stars. Brown dwarfs have masses that range from between a few times the mass of Jupiter to slightly less than a tenth of the mass of the Sun, and can be thought of as scaled up versions of the giant gas planets. They have surface temperatures of only about 730 degrees Celsius (1,345 degrees Fahrenheit), which, when combined with their size of 50 to 70 per cent of the Sun's diameter, means that brown dwarfs are very dim indeed.

Astronomers have found that the best method for locating brown dwarfs involves the utilization of infrared telescopes to detect the heat generated by these objects as they slowly contract under gravity. Many examples have been uncovered, mostly embedded within star-forming clouds. In stellar time-scales, the brown dwarfs do not radiate their meagre heat for long, and they can fade from a dim red object to an unobservable black star over about 10 million years. A high proportion of brown dwarf pairs have also been observed, where the separation between the gravitationally locked stars may be as small as five times the Earth-to-Sun distance. Other studies have revealed evidence for dusty disks around some brown dwarfs, thus raising the possibility that they too host miniature planetary systems. An interesting example discovered using NASA's Spitzer Space Telescope is called HD 3651, which is a Sun-like star that has been directly imaged to reveal a 50-Jupiter-mass brown dwarf companion star. Located in the constellation of Pisces, this system also harbours a planet of about the mass of Saturn. Interestingly, it seems that the gravity of the stellar companion to the brown dwarf is acting to disturb the planet's orbit into a highly elliptical path.

Understanding the population of brown dwarf stars in galaxies is also important in advancing ideas about the fate of the Universe. Observations of the motions of stars and galaxies have shown that they are gravitationally influenced by substantial amounts of matter that has not yet been identified in our telescopes. It is thought that a large component of this 'missing mass', or dark matter, could be composed of substantial numbers of very dim brown dwarf stars. Since these failed stars do not have nuclear energy sources to enable them to shine brightly, they can remain hidden in distant galaxies. To get a better idea of how the expansion of the Universe will proceed in time, it is necessary to accurately determine how much mass there is in the Universe. Thus the detection of potentially very populous 'dark' stellar objects such as brown dwarfs is very important in our attempt to understand the fate of the Universe.

Our Star, The Sun

Through many generations humankind has developed a growing understanding of the importance of the Sun as the dominant source of heat and light for life on Earth. We could not exist without the Sun, and its nature and evolution is vital to our survival. From our more local perspective on Earth, we need to understand how the Sun works, why it changes and how these variations might influence our lives on the planet. On a wider footing, the Sun, as an average star, is fundamental to our understanding of the stellar Universe. It is by far the closest star to us on Earth, and the only one for which we are able to directly witness phenomena occurring on its surface.

Our proximity to the Sun allows us to determine detailed information about it, which can then be applied and extrapolated to other stars in our Galaxy. Conversely, understanding the variety and life cycles of the stars enables us to learn about the origin, past and future of the Sun. In the widest context, the Sun is a very run-of-the-mill star, with no special location within our Milky Way Galaxy of at least 200 billion other stars. The Sun is embedded within one of the spiral arms, almost 26,000 light-years from the centre of the Galaxy. Together, the location, size, temperature and overall stability of the Sun provide an ideal environment for supporting life on Earth.

Characteristics
and Observations

Like the majority of stars, the Sun is primarily a vast ball of very hot hydrogen gas. Dominating the solar system, it provides more than 99 per cent of the total mass within it. This great mass is more than 1,000 times that of Jupiter, and provides the gravitational pull necessary to keep the planets in orbit around our star. Almost 70 per cent of the mass of the Sun is made up of hydrogen; nearly all the rest is helium. Less than a tenth of a per cent of the mass of the Sun is composed of heavier elements such as carbon, nitrogen, silicon and iron.

All stars have different layers or zones, including interior regions such as the core, which we cannot directly observe. The region of the Sun that we can actually view from Earth is its gaseous surface, which is comprised of layers known as the photosphere, the chromosphere, and a very tenuous outer region called the corona. The Sun's diameter is equivalent to 109 Earth diameters, which, when combined with its surface temperature of 5,800 degrees Celsius (10,500 degrees Fahrenheit), means that it is classified as a yellow-white G2, dwarf-type star. Temperatures in the Sun's very dense core rise to 15 million degrees Celsius (27 million degrees Fahrenheit), thus providing the conditions for nuclear fusion of hydrogen to helium, and the subsequent release of vast amounts of energy to make the Sun shine.

The Sun is a prodigious generator of energy. If we could harness the total energy output of the Sun for just one second, it would be equivalent to the annual energy manufactured by almost 3 billion large conventional power plants on Earth.

There has been a great wealth of new and highly revealing observations of the Sun over the past decade or so. These advances have been made possible mostly by the launch of several space observatories dedicated to monitoring a range of dynamic solar phenomena. For more than 11 years, the joint ESA and NASA mission called Solar and Heliospheric Observatory (SOHO) has studied violent and turbulent events in the outer regions of the Sun. It has also allowed astronomers to uniquely glimpse regions of the solar interior. Another collaborative ESA and NASA mission, Ulysses, has been studying streams of energetic particles that flow away from the Sun along magnetic field lines. This was the first spacecraft to journey over the north and south poles of the Sun. Launched in October 2006, NASA's Solar Terrestrial Relations Observatory (STEREO) will provide unprecedented views of the Sun and its influence on Earth. Two identical spacecraft have been deployed to provide three-dimensional images of the structure of eruptions on the Sun.

Aside from increasing our knowledge of the workings and processes of the Sun, these space observatories are permitting scientists to understand the effects of the Sun on the surrounding regions of interplanetary space. The probes have given rise to the relatively new discipline of studying space weather, which is concerned with the changing conditions in the regions of space that affect the Earth.

RIGHT: *Clementine spacecraft view of the Sun rising over the Moon and the planet Venus placed on the right.*

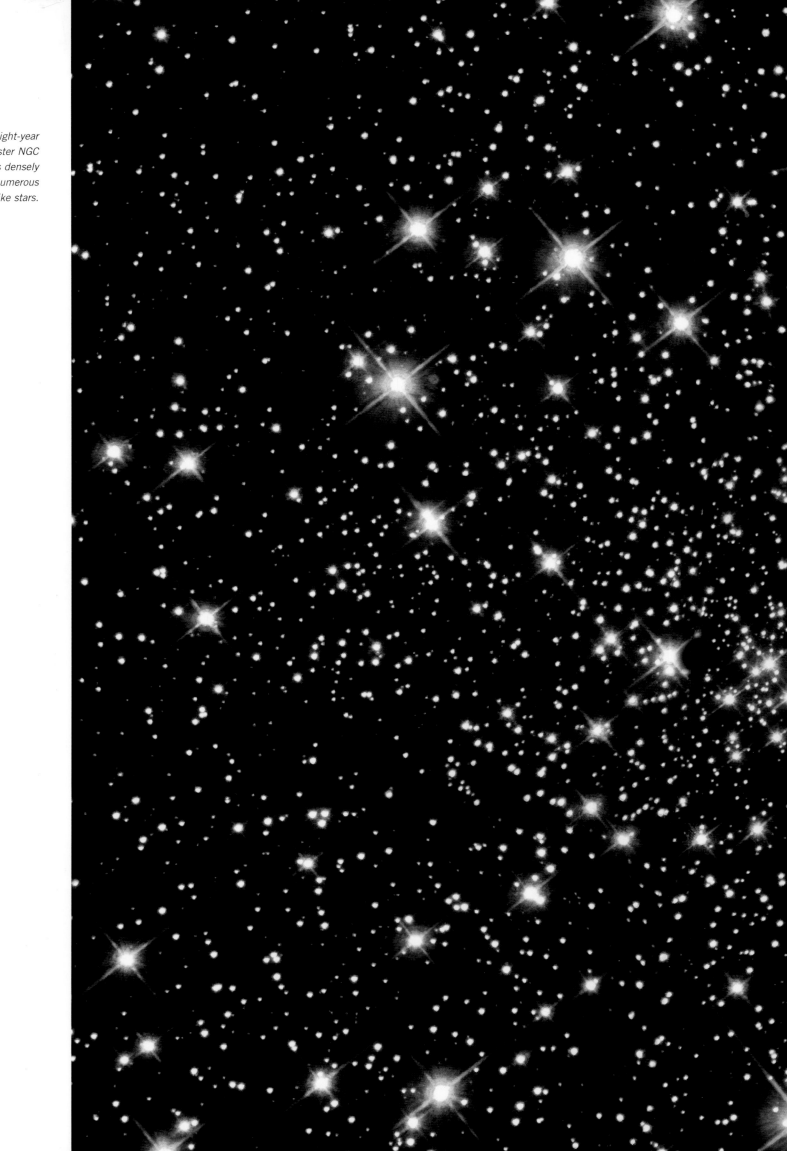

RIGHT: *The 8,200 light-year distant globular cluster NGC 6397, which is densely packed with numerous Sun-like stars.*

A Nuclear Powerhouse

In studying the total power output of the Sun, astrophysicists have attempted to discover how such an enormous power source could be maintained over several billion years. In other words, they have been trying to fathom how the Sun could shine so intensely over such an extended period of time. If the solar energy source was a combustive one – like burning coal or oil, for example – a star the size of the Sun would glow for barely 5,000 years before all the fuel had been used up. A major leap forward in our understanding of the inner workings of the Sun followed the development of Albert Einstein's (1879–1955) theory of relativity in 1905. A pivotal implication of this theory was that a small amount of matter could be converted into an enormous amount of energy.

By around the 1920s, the astrophysicist Arthur Eddington (1882–1944) had suggested that the temperature in the central regions of the Sun may be much higher than previously thought. More than a decade later, Hans Bethe (1906–2005) and Carl von Weizsäcker (1912–2007), among others, had proposed that the Sun's store of energy was sub-atomic in nature. This notion, combined with important concepts of quantum physics, led to a realization that nuclear fusion was the source of energy production in the Sun. It wasn't until the mid 20th century, however, that details of the reactions by which hydrogen is fused into helium in the Sun's core were finally understood.

The core of the Sun is not only more than 15 million degrees Celsius (27 million degrees Fahrenheit), gas is held there at pressures of almost 250 billion times greater than that at sea level on Earth. With a density more than 150 times greater than water, these fierce conditions are exactly those that are needed to force hydrogen nuclei (protons) to move incredibly fast, penetrate each other and fuse together.

The transformation that takes place inside the Sun involves four nuclei of hydrogen fusing in a three-step chain reaction to produce a helium nucleus. In each transformation, a tiny amount of mass is given up, which is converted into a large amount of energy. Today, every second, the Sun is converting almost 700 million tons of hydrogen in its core to 695 million tons of helium. The remaining 5 million tons is transformed into vast mega watts of energy, providing the Sun's luminous output. This thermonuclear reaction produces electromagnetic energy in the form of gamma rays, as opposed to visible light.

Thankfully for us on Earth, we are not being blasted by lethal gamma rays from the Sun; we are saved because the Sun is so large and dense that energy released at its centre takes hundreds of thousands of years to jostle its way up to the surface. During this highly convoluted path, the gamma ray photons encounter countless collisions with hydrogen and helium nuclei, losing a little bit of energy with each collision. Once the energy has finally reached the solar surface and is radiated away, it has been reduced from high-energy gamma rays to the visible yellow-white light with which we are so familiar.

The Sun (and the solar system) was formed about 4.6 billion years ago. Since it is of a finite size, its nuclear energy supply is also finite. Astronomers estimate that the Sun has enough nuclear fuel left to keep it shining at its current rate for about 5 billion more years. We will see in *The Evolution and Demise of Stars*, (*see page 135*), that for the Sun and all other stars, the end of energy generation via nuclear fusion will mark the onset of rapid changes. The Sun will no longer be able to support itself against its own gravity, and will begin a gradual slide towards its demise.

The light we receive here on Earth is emitted from the uppermost layers of the Sun; we are unable to see its very dense inner regions. Thus, our knowledge of the Sun's interior is primarily based on mathematical models developed by astrophysicists. Measured quantities, such as the Sun's mass and chemical make-up, are combined with the laws of physics to predict condition in its core and the surrounding zones. Sophisticated computer codes have been developed to calculate solar temperature, pressure and density at any internal position, including the core.

Using other methods of analysis, we can tell that the Sun is continually vibrating, somewhat like a ringing bell. Astronomers are able to detect regions of the Sun's surface moving up and down by several kilometres over just a few minutes. Sound waves travelling through the Sun are setting up millions of resonating waves. Just as geologists analyse earthquakes to study the Earth's internal layers, so these solar vibrations can be measured and interpreted to probe the physical conditions down to the Sun's centre. This study, known as helioseismology, is now helping astronomers monitor the pulsating surfaces of other stars as well.

An alternative way to study the interior of the Sun is via the detection of exotic particles that are created as a by-product of the nuclear fusion reactions occurring at the core. The fusion of hydrogen results not only in a helium nucleus and gamma rays, but also in two other particles known as positrons and neutrinos. Positrons are counterparts to electrons, and are quickly annihilated when they collide with electrons inside the Sun. Neutrinos, however, rarely interact with ordinary matter, and speed through the Sun's layers. They have no electric charge, and are very nearly mass-less. Every second, billions of neutrinos pass through every square centimetre of our

bodies, but they don't interact with us or harm us. Vast underground reactors have been built to try and detect neutrinos escaping from the Sun's core. One example is the Super-Kamiokande Solar Neutrino Detector, comprised of a tank filled with 50,000 tons of ultra-pure water, and located deep in a disused mine in Japan.

Physicists have discovered that fusion reactions in the Sun produce one flavour of neutrinos with a tiny amount of mass. These elusive particles can change their flavour to a different type of neutrino as they travel to the Earth at speeds close to that of light. Since neutrinos are so incredibly abundant, even if each particle has a tiny mass of several million times less than that of an electron, their total effect from all the stars can be very important for the evolution of the Universe and our understanding of matter.

ABOVE: *Computer simulations of numerous patches of the Sun's surface moving away from us (red) and approaching us (blue).*

The Changing Solar Surface

Viewed from Earth's ideal location 150 million kilometres (93 million miles) away, the Sun may appear constant and almost passive, but our star is in reality very dynamic. Its surface layers are constantly changing as hot cells of gas bubble up and cooler ones sink below. Occasionally, more energetic phenomena are witnessed, such as streamers of electrified gas looping up through the solar atmosphere and magnetic force fields giving rise to spicules of matter rising from the surface, common features of the relatively 'quiet Sun'. We also know that the Sun regularly builds up its activity over a period of years, peaking with energetic phenomena such as explosive flares and giant ejections of particles into the solar system.

The deepest layer of the Sun that we can observe directly is known as the photosphere. This is the mottled, gaseous surface from which the photons generated by nuclear reactions in the Sun's core escape into space. The photosphere is about 400 kilometres (250 miles) thick, with an average temperature of 5800 degrees Celsius (10,500 degrees Fahrenheit).

From the Earth, the most common features observable on the photosphere are dark patches known as sunspots. These Earth-sized blotches feature in astronomical recordings of, amongst others, the ancient Chinese and Greek astronomers. In the early 17th century, Galileo Galilei, in conjunction with other observers including Benedetto Castelli (1578–1643) and Christopher Scheiner (1573–1650), carried out detailed telescopic observations of the sunspots. Galileo concluded that these 'imperfections' changed their shapes and positions with time, and must essentially be on the surface of the Sun.

We know today that sunspots occur in regions of the solar surface where strong magnetic field lines emerge, which has the effect of lowering the temperature in that area. The sunspots are therefore cooler than the

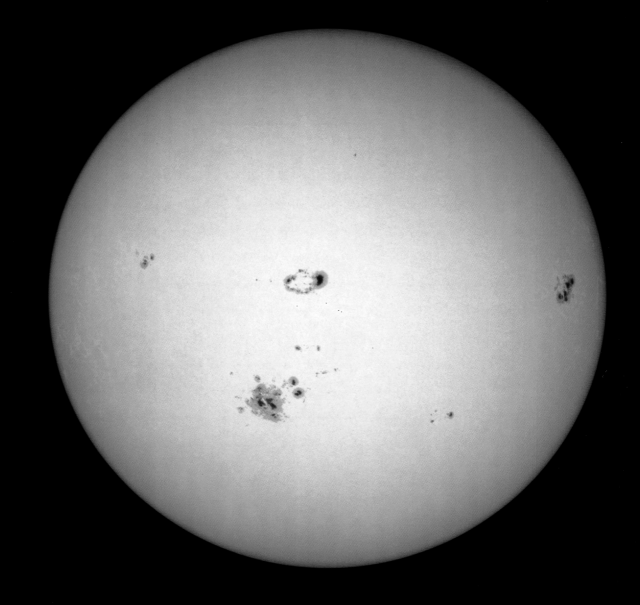

RIGHT: *Large sunspot groups, some spanning 15 Earth diameters, are seen in this SOHO spacecraft image of the Sun.*

FAR RIGHT: *A remarkably detailed view from the Swedish Solar Telescope of the umbra and penumbra of a sunspot.*

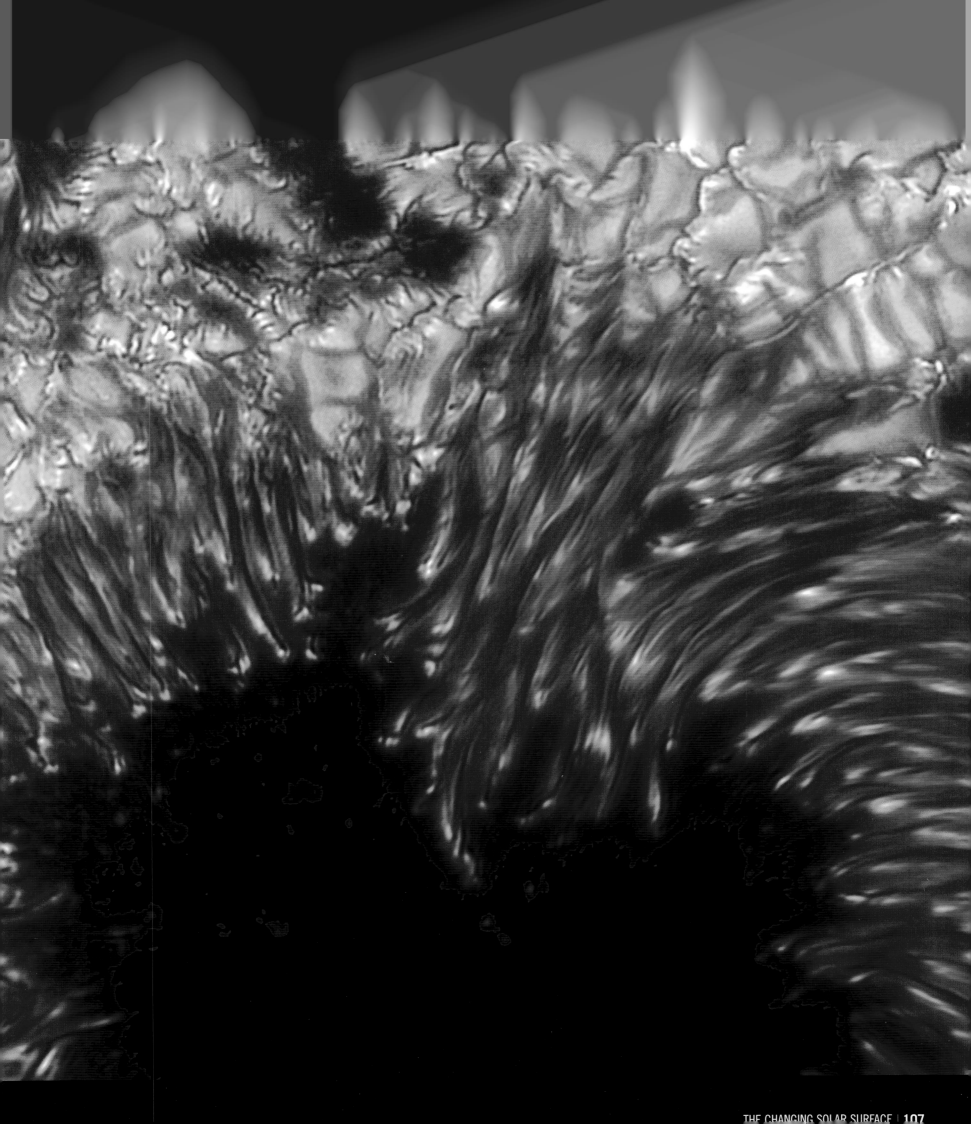

surrounding photosphere by about 1,530 degrees Celsius (1,800 degrees Fahrenheit). The central darkest part of a sunspot is called the umbra, and is surrounded by a slightly lighter penumbra of lower magnetic strength. Sunspots thus appear as dark patches only in contrast against the hotter and brighter regions around them; in other words, they are not really black. In fact, if you could cut out a sunspot and place it against the dark sky, it would glow a red-orange colour. Since the early observations of Galileo, astronomers have monitored the movements of sunspots across the photosphere in order to map out how the Sun rotates. Often occurring in groups, a typical sunspot gathering may be 10,000 kilometres (6,200 miles) in diameter, and can last between many hours to several weeks.

Gaseous bodies such as stars and giant planets like Jupiter and Saturn do not spin as rigid balls, nor do all of the latitudes of the Sun rotate at the same rate. The equatorial regions spin faster, within a period of about 25 days. Regions at latitudes of 30 degrees both above and below the solar equator rotate once every 26.5 days. The regions near the poles complete a rotation in 30 days. This property is known as differential rotation, and is fundamental to understanding how activity in the Sun changes over many years.

If the Sun rotated like a solid ball, the strength of its magnetic field would remain fairly steady and weak, not unlike the Earth's magnetic field. Since the Sun's rotation varies with latitude, the magnetic field lines which are threaded beneath the photosphere become very twisted. Over a cycle lasting about 11 years, the magnetic field lines go from being an ordered and untangled arrangement to becoming highly wound up and kinked, before finally being restored back to an ordered state again.

Records of the Sun extending back centuries have revealed that the number of sunspots also varies with an approximately 11-year pattern, and indeed, the global activity of the Sun follows this cycle. At the start of an 11-year cycle, the Sun has fewer sunspots and a general dearth of other dynamic events, such as large eruptions. This state is referred to as the solar minimum. Gradually, over about five years or so, the average number of sunspots seen on the Sun's surface rises to a peak, with most appearing within only five degrees of the equator. At the time of this 'solar maximum', we can expect more violent forms of activity, including powerful flares. Solar scientists predict that the next solar maximum will occur between 2010 and 2011, and it is forecast to be a spectacular one.

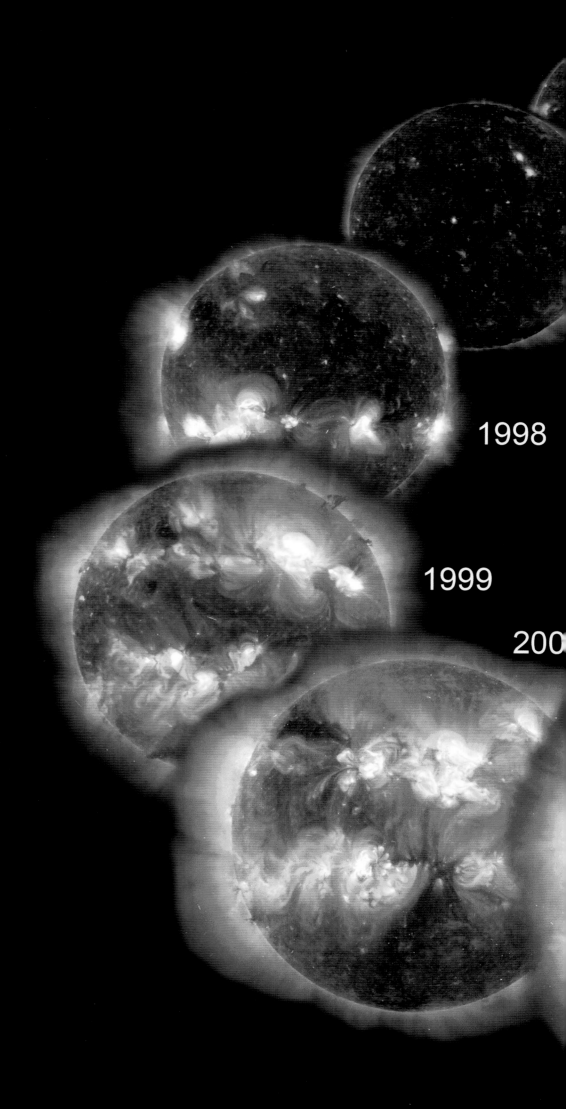

1998

1999

200

RIGHT: *The SOHO spacecraft montage of the 11-year cycle of the Sun.*

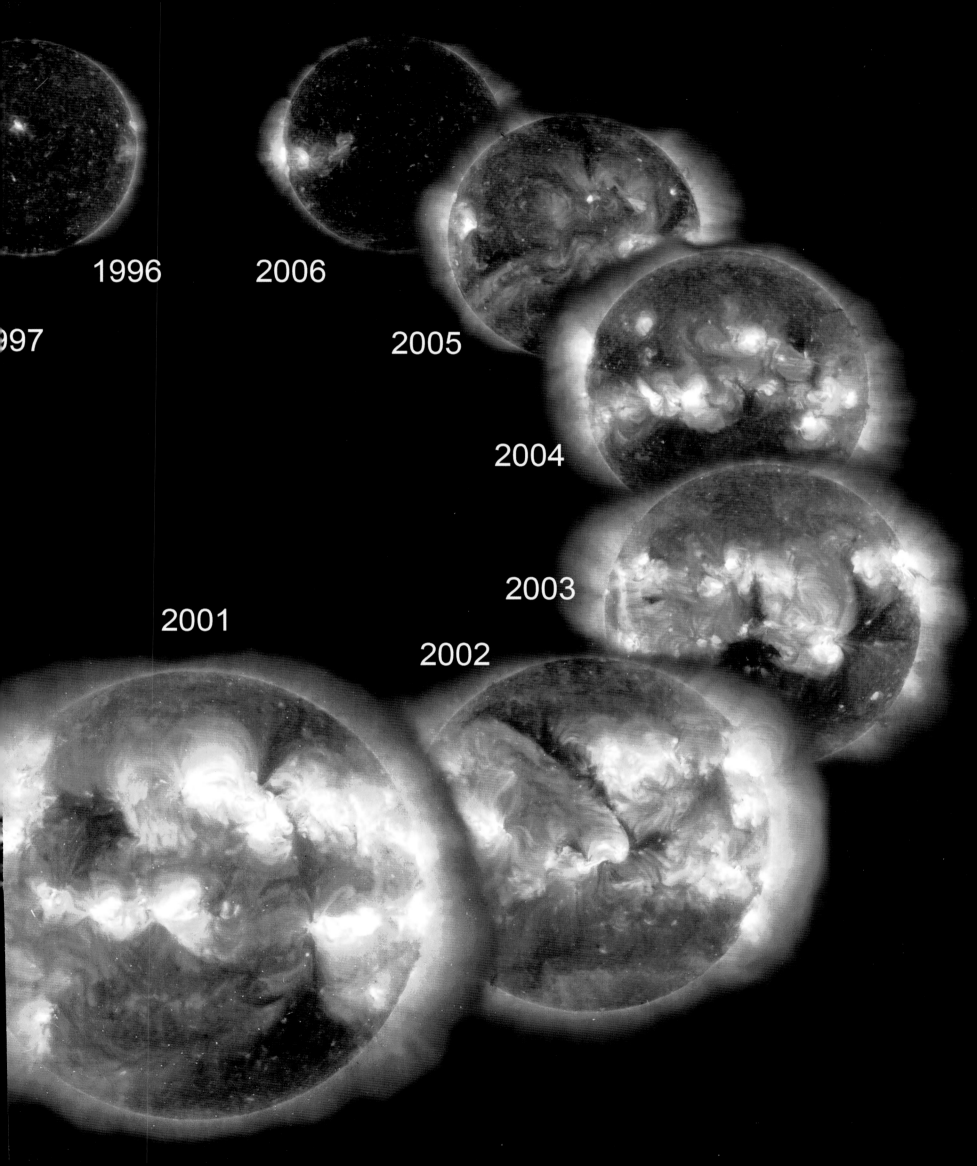

An Eerie Light

One of the most wondrous sights in nature occurs when the New Moon is perfectly aligned between the Earth and the Sun to cover up the photosphere. The spectacle of a total eclipse of the Sun results from the fortuitous coincidence that the angle projected in the sky by the disc of the Moon is almost exactly equal to that projected by the bright surface of the Sun. This event is able to occur because although the Moon is almost 400 times smaller than the Sun, it is also about 400 times closer to us.

The total solar eclipse presents us with our finest views of the tenuous outer layers of the Sun known as the corona. During the eclipse, an eerie, ghostly white light is seen shimmering around the dark Moon. This is the light of the very low-density uppermost atmosphere of the Sun, which extends millions of kilometres above the photosphere. Outside of a total eclipse, the corona cannot be seen, since its feeble light is totally overwhelmed by the million-times-brighter photosphere. The corona exhibits complex structures in the form of wispy streamers extending in various directions, the shapes of which change over several days.

An enigmatic property of the solar corona is that its temperature is an incredible million degrees. Given that the Sun's temperature decreases from 15 million degrees Celsius (27 million degrees Fahrenheit) at its core to 5,800 degrees Celsius (10,500 degrees Fahrenheit) at the photosphere, one would expect the temperature of the corona, which is even further away from the Sun, to be much lower. The reason the million-degree-hot gas in the corona doesn't shine very brightly is that it is has a very low density. There are relatively so few atoms in the corona that the total amount of energy contained in all of the moving particles is very low. Travelling to the Sun, one would hardly notice the heat from the gas in the corona, but would soon be sizzled by the fierce light from the considerably denser photosphere.

ABOVE: *Composite image of the Sun assembled during the total eclipse on 21 June 2001.*

The current consensus of scientists is that the very high temperature of the corona is linked to the magnetic properties of the Sun. It remains uncertain, however, precisely how the energy in the magnetic field is converted to heat in the corona. One possibility is that magnetic field lines approach very close to each other and end up being broken up and rearranged. The reconnection of field

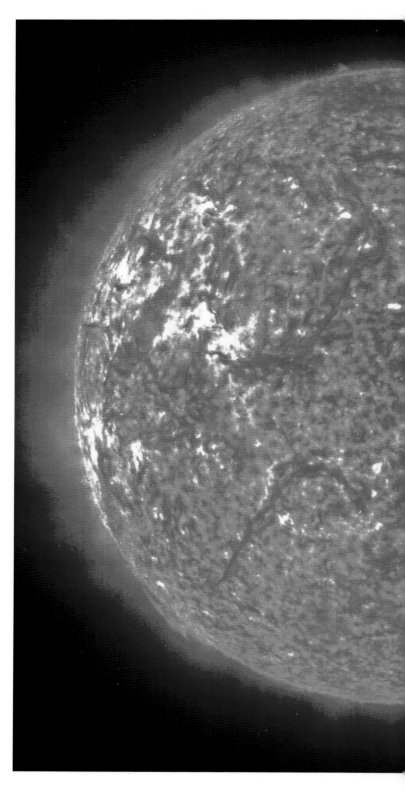

lines has never been directly observed, but it may represent the mechanism by which energy is transferred into the coronal gas.

The high-temperature, fast-moving particles of the corona can reach high enough speeds to escape the Sun's powerful gravitational attraction. Moving at over 400 kilometres per second (250 miles per second), these electrically charged particles escape the Sun and stream

away to distant parts of the solar system. This outflow of matter is known as the solar wind, and it amounts to about a million tons of material being ejected every second. The mass of the Sun is so much greater in comparison, however, that the total mass lost via the outflow of particles will barely amount to a few tenths of a per cent of the Sun's mass over its lifetime.

The solar wind does, however, play a significant role in the planetary system, since the electrically charged particles can interact with the magnetic fields of the planets and get deflected into their upper atmospheres. When the solar particles strike atoms in the Earth's atmosphere, visible light is produced, resulting in shimmering red, green and white glowing areas in the sky. These are the aurorae (or northern and southern lights) that can mostly be seen from high latitudes in the two hemispheres of the planet. When the Sun is at its 'solar maximum' in its 11-year cycle, the number and energies of the solar wind particles is greater, thus raising the possibility of more spectacular auroral displays in our skies. Similar aurorae have also been discovered in the atmospheres of other planets, including Jupiter and Saturn.

LEFT: *A vast twirling prominence is seen erupting (lower right) in this SOHO spacecraft image.*

ABOVE: *A unique view of an aurora over the Earth's north pole, captured by NASA's Polar spacecraft.*

The Violent Sun

Recent spacecraft missions such as SOHO and STEREO have provided fascinating insights into the power of the Sun. Near solar maximum, the magnetically related activity of the Sun can be channelled into tremendously powerful explosions, which in turn can have consequences for us on Earth. One of the most violent eruptive events is known as a flare. These brief explosions on the Sun's surface occur when the energy stored in highly twisted magnetic fields is suddenly released, resulting in bursts of radiation. From gamma rays and X-rays to radio waves, powerful disturbances spread out through the solar system. Energy equivalent to a billion tons of TNT can be released in just a few minutes.

Flares on the Sun are classified according to how bright they are in the X-ray waveband. The weakest flares are called C-class, and have essentially minimal effects on Earth. M-class flares are stronger, and are capable of causing radio communication blackouts in the planet's polar regions. The most explosive flares are labelled X-class, and can have potentially serious consequences for us, including global communication blackouts and the creation of powerful electromagnetic storms in the Earth's upper atmosphere. A substantial X-class flare could last for over an hour, with the corresponding ejection of protons and electrons from the Sun's outer layers. In March 1989, an X-class solar flare was powerful enough to disable an electrical power generation grid in Quebec, Canada. A similar solar storm in May 1998 seriously damaged the telecommunication satellite Galaxy IV. These examples serve to remind us of yet another direct link between the Sun and the Earth, and the influence of the Sun upon our everyday lives.

The most dramatic and explosive events on the Sun are associated with the eruption of enormous amounts of material into interplanetary space. Known as coronal mass ejections, or CMEs, vast bubbles of gas may be ejected from the solar atmosphere over a timescale of just a few hours. When close to the solar maximum, the Sun can yield three to five CMEs per day. Billions of tons of electrified gas accelerate out at velocities of millions of kilometres per hour. Having escaped the Sun's gravity, the bubble of gas

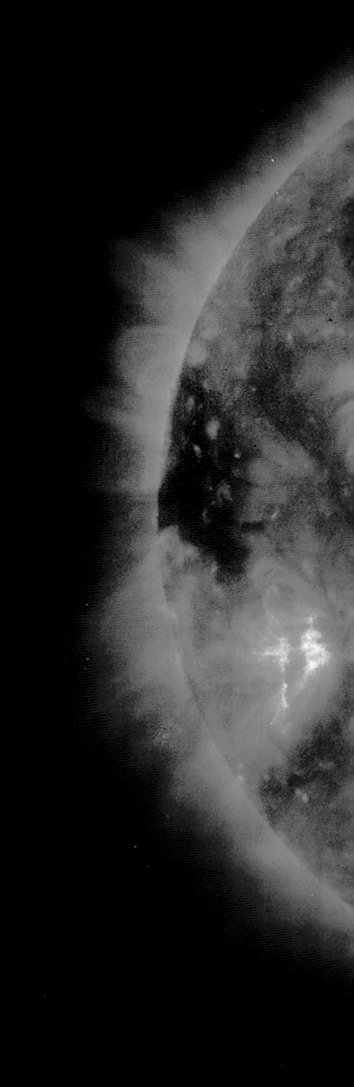

RIGHT: *False colour image of a large X-class solar flare witnessed on 4 November 2003.*

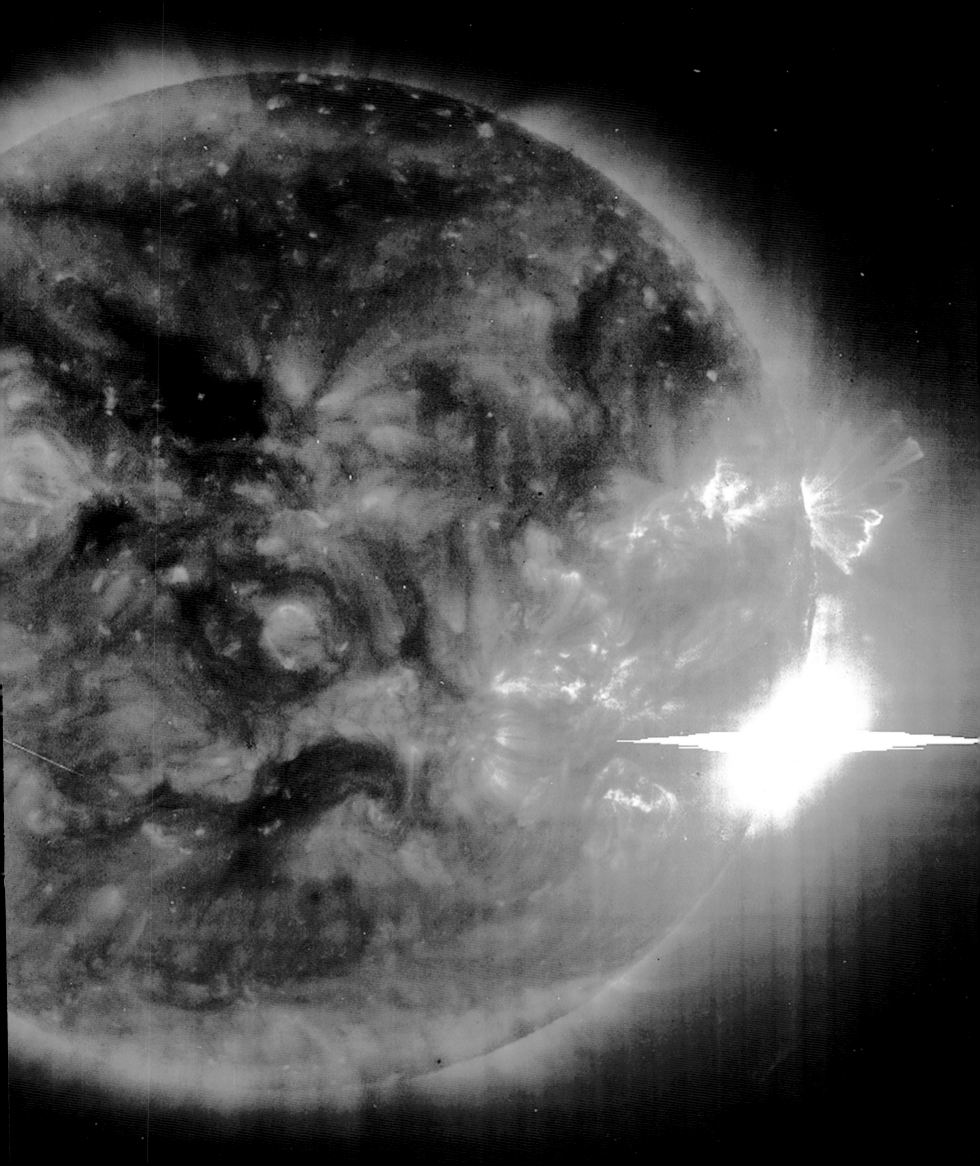

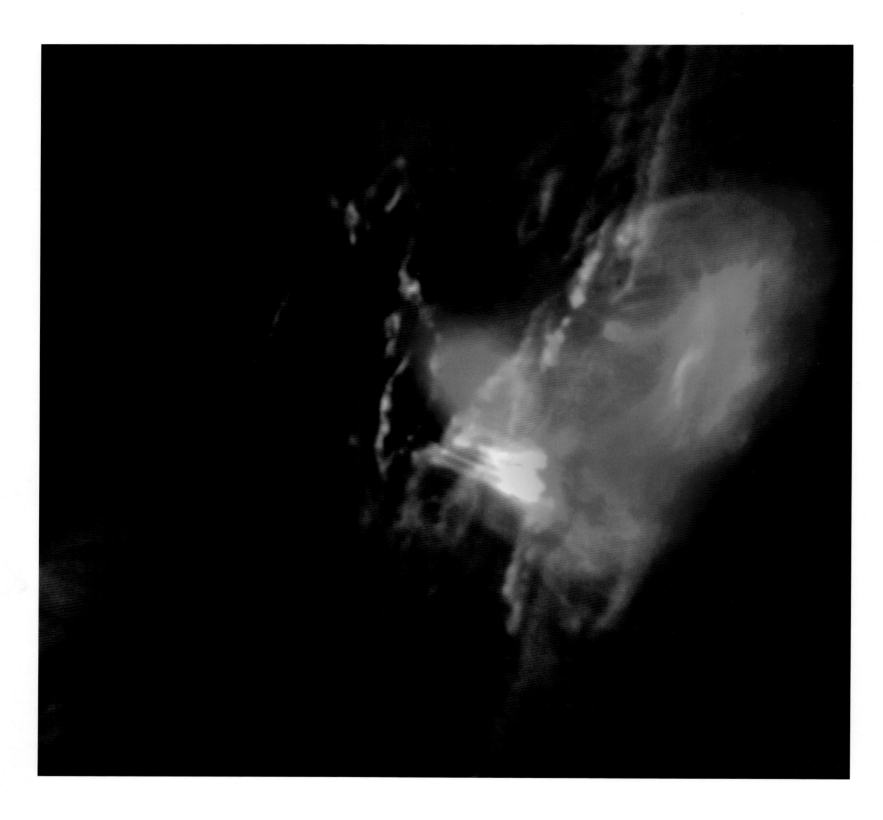

from a CME can expand to match the diameter of the Sun itself, producing a high energy shock wave as it ploughs through the solar wind and on toward the rest of the solar system. Sometimes (but not always), the CME may also be accompanied by explosive flares on the Sun's surface.

There remain uncertainties in our understanding of the origin of CMEs. The current consensus of solar scientists is that a network of magnetic loops restrains a gradually building mass of gas and prevents it from rising up to the corona. The tied-down plasma therefore stores up a tremendous amount of energy, which eventually breaks through as a CME when the overlying magnetic loops finally break up and rearrange themselves. Occasionally, a CME might occur on the side of the Sun facing the Earth. If the expanding cloud of matter follows a path that intersects the Earth's orbit, the result can be an increase in spectacular terrestrial phenomena, such as vivid aurorae and a significant rise in the radiation levels of our atmosphere.

ABOVE: *Image of a powerful flare erupting on the Sun, where red and white regions represent million degree hot gas.*

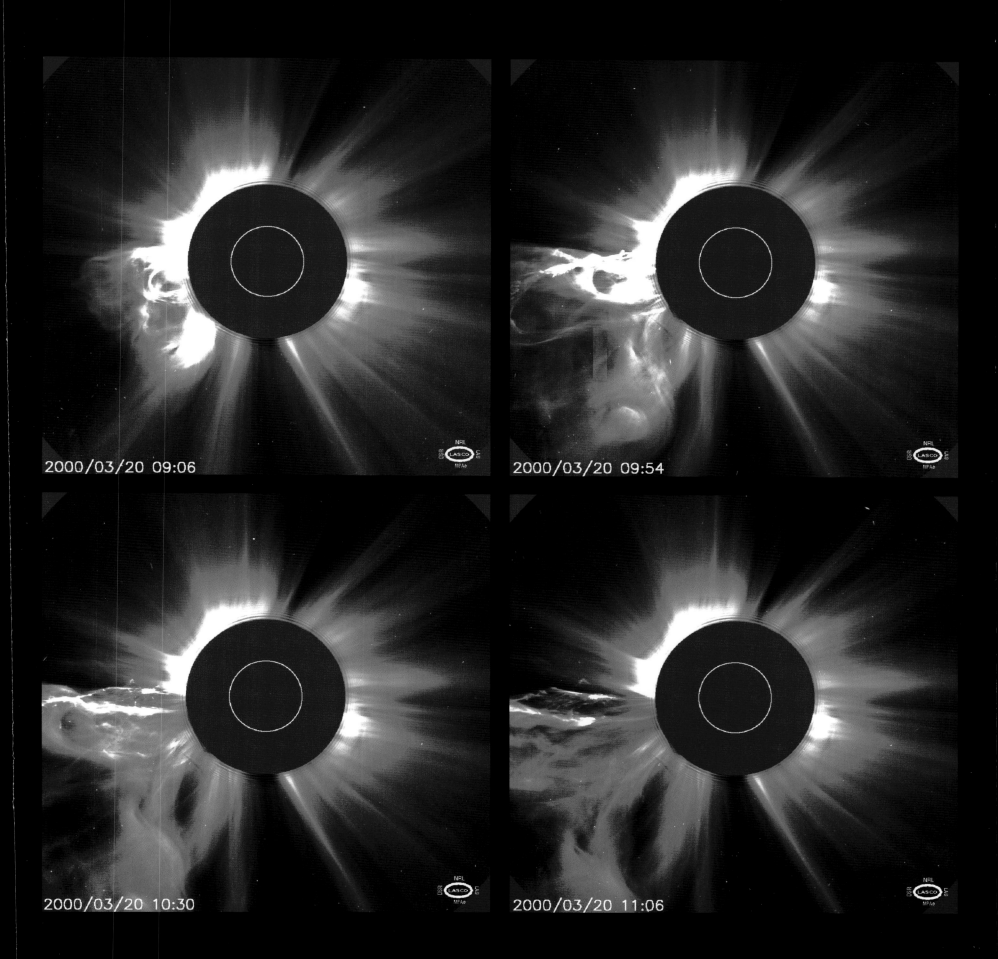

2000/03/20 09:06

2000/03/20 09:54

2000/03/20 10:30

2000/03/20 11:06

ABOVE: *A time-sequence of SOHO images covering the launch of a coronal mass ejection over a period of 2 hours.*

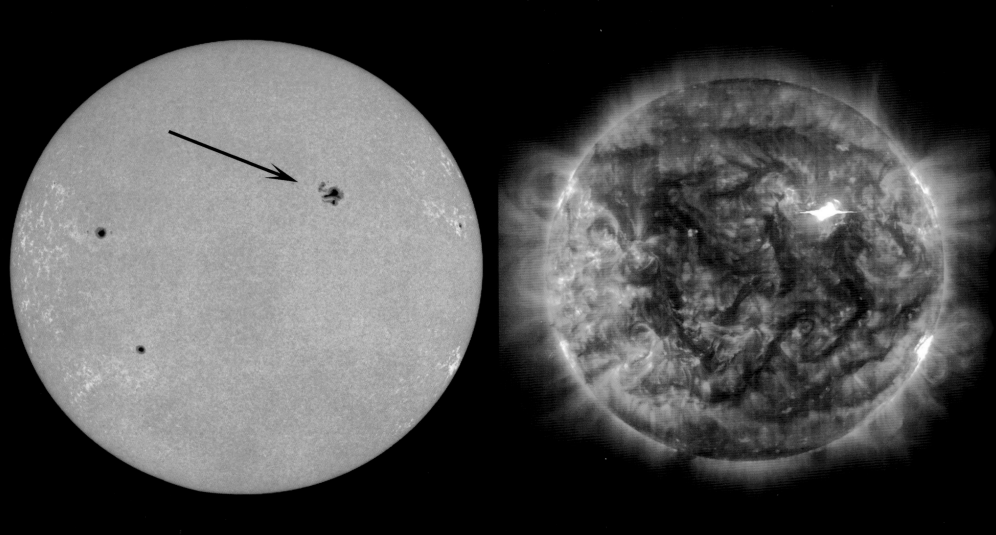

The Sun— Earth Link

The detailed study of the changing Sun is today partially motivated by the need to understand the Earth's space environment. The processes and phenomena occurring on the Sun clearly impact the Earth, while also providing us with a laboratory for learning about the evolution of other stars and their planetary systems. Major disturbances such as CMEs can reach the Earth between two to four days after escaping from the Sun. The consequences of this and other activities, such as flares and magnetic storms, are growing in severity as our reliance on technologies and satellite communications increases. From commercial and safety viewpoints, there is now a firm realization that the interaction between the Sun and the Earth needs to be monitored, with the ultimate goal of developing an understanding of how changes in space weather can affect the Earth.

Aside from the disruptions to radio, television and other communication systems, major solar storms can generate geomagnetic anomalies capable of affecting navigation, such as the accuracy of GPS signals. Increases in the geomagnetic activity and ultraviolet radiation from the Sun can heat the Earth's upper atmosphere, making it expand and thus causing the particle density to rise significantly at the distances where man-made satellites orbit. The effect can be to increase the drag on satellites, which can in turn alter their orbits. Furthermore, the high-energy radiation from solar flares is not only dangerous to astronauts working in space; it can also potentially result in increased levels of radiation in high-altitude aircraft.

More speculative is the mooted link between our climate on Earth and changes in the overall activity of the Sun. High-energy particles entering the Earth's middle atmosphere can interact with the molecules already there to form new chemicals that can act to destroy the ozone. We noted earlier that the Sun has an 11-year cycle, when

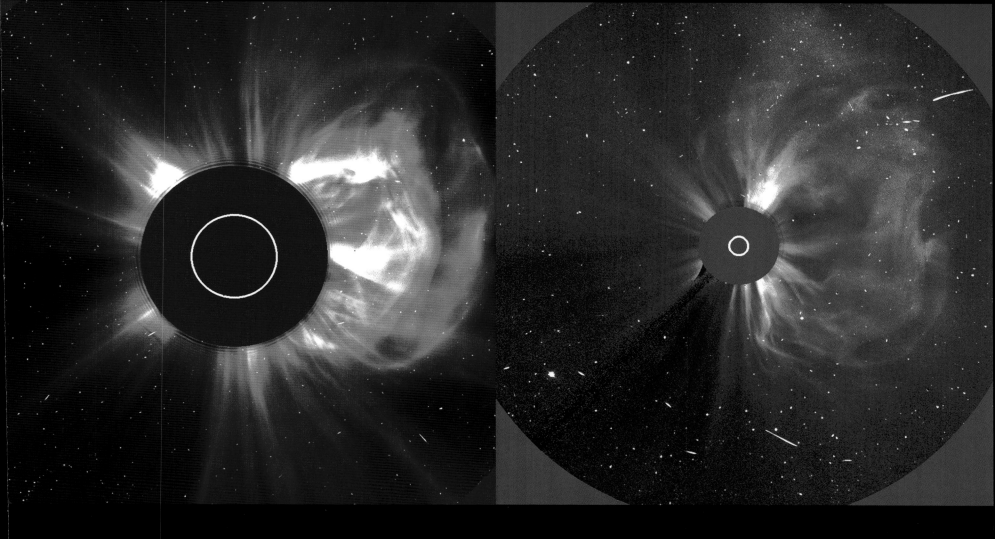

its magnetic and sunspot activity goes from minimum to maximum and back to minimum again. While the increase in radiant solar energy received by the Earth beyond its atmosphere is barely two tenths of a per cent between solar minimum and maximum, scientists are nonetheless studying the effects of these changes on, for example, the circulation of our atmosphere and its interaction with the oceans and land.

An interesting epoch in solar activity is apparent from historical records, which show that between 1645 and 1715, there was a virtual absence of sunspots recorded on the disk of the Sun. Known as the Maunder Minimum, this apparent drop in magnetic activity on the Sun coincided with a mini ice-age in Europe. The implication here is that there was a fall in the total output of the Sun that directly affected the Earth's climate. Considerable work remains to be done in order to unambiguously distinguish between fluctuations in the Sun's activity and human contributions to the greenhouse effect in altering the Earth's global climate.

New Worlds Around Distant Stars

We saw in *Birth Rings and Jets*, page 40, that a collapsing cloud of gas and dust not only leads to the formation of a star, but also to a spinning disk of debris. Observational evidence and theoretical models suggest that the subsequent formation of planets is almost inevitable, forged out of the material in the flat disk surrounding the newborn star.

The expectation that planets commonly form near stars has been raised considerably over the past decade or so by the secure (but indirect) detection of new planets beyond our solar system. Known as exoplanets, or extra-solar planets, more than 250 new worlds have been discovered since 1995, and the rate of discovery is increasing at an astounding rate. Given our Milky Way Galaxy's population of more than 200 billion stars, and the apparently close association been the birth of stars and the formation of planets, there is growing excitement at the possibility of detecting Earth-sized terrestrial planets orbiting around Sun-like stars elsewhere in the Galaxy. This quest immediately leads to the question of whether life-sustaining, habitable planets might be common, or, alternatively, whether solar systems such as ours are exceptionally rare.

The primary difficulty in detecting exoplanets is that they are extremely faint. Planets shine by reflected starlight, and they are typically a billion times fainter in visible light than their parent stars. Furthermore, even in the case of the nearby stars in our solar neighbourhood, a planet would not appear as widely separated from its host star even in our largest telescopes. Exoplanets are thus mostly lost in the glare of the stars they orbit. For this reason, astronomers have developed indirect observation methods that have successfully permitted the detection of numerous exoplanets. These innovative techniques have unravelled not only giant Jupiter-like planets, but also more than 20 systems of multiple planets and, more recently, substantial terrestrial or rocky planets. It has also been possible to determine the chemical make-up of exoplanets by passing their feeble light through a spectrograph.

LEFT: *At a distance of 420 light-years, the Coronet cluster is one of the nearest regions for studying the birth of stars and planets.*

Discovering Exoplanets

Most of the exoplanets discovered to date have been detected via the use of a method that monitors the tiny movements, or wobbles, that a planet typically imposes upon a host star. The planet exerts a gravitational tug on the star as it orbits around a common centre of mass. Since the star is considerably more massive than the planet, the centre of mass of the two bodies will be very close to the star, but not at its very centre. Both the star and the planet will orbit around this mutual balance point.

Since the star is comparatively so much more massive than the planet, its orbit, or wobble, around the mutual balance point will be very small. Nevertheless, the tiny movements imposed upon the star betray the presence of an unseen body, or bodies. The size of the stellar wobble provides a handle on the planet's mass, and the time over which the star completes a full orbit around the centre of the mass gives the planet's orbital period. Astronomers use very precise spectrograph measurements to record the shift in the star's spectral lines. As the star moves very slightly towards our telescopes, the spectral lines shift toward the bluer colours. Conversely, as the star wobbles away from us, under the influence of its planet or planets, the spectral lines recorded in the telescope move toward the more reddish colours, or toward longer wavelengths.

Very precise measurements are demanded by the spectrograph, as typical stellar movements are barely a few metres per second. For example, an extra-terrestrial observer monitoring the Sun would find that it wobbles by 12.5 metres (40 feet) per second over a 12-year time period. This perturbation is due to the gravitational tug of Jupiter. A second, even weaker, shift in the Sun occurs over the 27-year orbit of Saturn. This radial velocity or Doppler technique is most attuned to uncovering massive Jupiter-like planets, since they can exert a detectable tug on their stars. The method also works well for large planets orbiting close to their stars, as the gravitational pull weakens as the distance between the two bodies grows.

Another indirect yet probing method exploits the chance alignment whereby an orbiting exoplanet passes precisely between our planet and its host star. As the planet crosses in front of the stellar disk, it is possible to measure a small decrease in the brightness of the star. Similar transits can be observed in our solar system when Mercury and Venus pass in front of the Sun in our direct view from Earth. If our intrepid extra-terrestrial observer was positioned so as to view the solar system exactly edge-on, the presence of Jupiter would be indirectly revealed as the gas planet crossed the face of the Sun (which it does once every 12 years), resulting in a 1 per cent decrease in our star's brightness. This transit method was first successfully employed to study a star called HD209548, which exists about 150 light-years away in the constellation of Pegasus. The star's brightness decreased by 1.7 per cent every 3.5 days, which is easily detectable using even modest equipment.

The amount by which a star's brightness drops during a transit can also be interpreted to provide an estimate of the size of the exoplanet. For example, measurements from the Doppler and transit methods have been combined to reveal that a planet of about 200 Earth masses and a radius of 1.3 times that of Jupiter is orbiting HD209458. The implied planet density is 0.3 grams per cubic centimetre, much less than that of water, and confirms that the exoplanet around HD209458 is a 'hot Jupiter', with an atmospheric temperature of about 1100 degrees Celsius (2030 degrees Fahrenheit). Further, Hubble Space Telescope observations of HD209458, taken during and out of transits, were compared to reveal spectroscopic signatures of the exoplanet, with the specific detection of sodium, thought to be present in high clouds.

A technique more suited to the detection of less massive, Earth-sized, planets is known as gravitational lensing. This method is rooted in the principles and predictions of Albert Einstein's general theory of relativity. Mass distorts or warps the space around it; the path of light travelling close to the mass also becomes deflected. Light rays appear bent in warped space near a massive object because the rays follow geodesics, or shortest paths, just as the line of the equator is a geodesic around the globe of the Earth. When the light rays originating from a star pass very close to another star or other massive body on its way to our telescopes, the gravity of the intervening object will bend the rays by a very slight amount. The intervening object therefore acts like a lens to magnify and amplify the light of the object aligned precisely behind it.

Astronomers have been using this subtle effect to search for planets by monitoring numerous stars for signs of temporary changes to their brightness. The chance

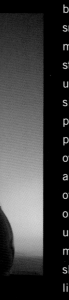

ABOVE: *The 10-metre diameter Keck I telescope perched on the Manua Kea peak in Hawaii, which is capable of very sensitive indirect measurements of exoplanets and their host stars.*

RIGHT: *Artist's impression of an extrasolar planet transiting across the face of a star.*

alignment of a background star with a foreground star that is being orbited by an exoplanet can produce a characteristic brightening of the background star. This change can be decoded to reveal indirect evidence for the presence of an exoplanet. This micro-lensing technique currently holds great promise for finding even the smallest and most distant planets, thus raising the possibility of uncovering an Earth-mass body.

One disadvantage of using micro-lensing, however, is that it requires the very special alignment between background and foreground stars (and their planets), which is why less than a dozen exoplanets have been discovered in this way so far. Yet one intriguing example of the method used successfully involved the discovery in 2006 of the new planet known as OGLE-2005-BLG-390Lb, which orbits a star almost 22,000 light-years from Earth. Micro-lensing measurements revealed the planet to be about five times the mass of the Earth, and most likely made of rock. This rare detection arose from the nightly pointing of a relatively modest 1.3-metre (4-foot)-diameter telescope toward the same dense patch of 100 million stars, in the direction of the centre of our Galaxy.

It is beyond the capability of current astronomical instruments to directly image the light from a distant exoplanet. Attempting to observe the exoplanet in the infrared waveband, as opposed to in visible wavelengths, will reduce the glare of light from the host star, as the exoplanet will appear somewhat brighter in the infrared waveband. Nevertheless, astronomers await the development of new technologies that can block out the light from the parent star so that we can view any orbiting planets more directly. The European Space Agency is, for example, considering plans for 'next generation' missions such as Darwin, which will aim to combine the signals from multiple precisely controlled telescopes in space. This innovative, but expensive, interferometric approach offers the very exciting prospect of delivering low-resolution images of Earth-sized planets around Sun-like stars. Though the images may still be barely a few pixels in size, the signal could be passed through spectrographs to determine the chemical make-up of the planets, and perhaps even reveal the bio-signatures of life.

LEFT: *Artist's impression of the six telescopes precisely controlled in space that the European Space Agency plans for the Darwin mission, which would aim to study the atmospheres of Earth-like exoplanets.*

The Habitable Zones of Stars and Galaxies

There is currently growing and understandable interest in the discovery of 'habitable exoplanets', which may be defined as those bodies that can sustain life on their surfaces or sub-surfaces for extended periods of time. Yet until the development of new planet hunting telescopes, which will surely come in the next couple of decades, we can really only debate the physical conditions that are requisite for habitable planets. Out of the current list of known exoplanets, very few can be regarded as terrestrial or Earth-like candidates. One example is a planet that has been indirectly detected around a host star called Gliese 581, a red dwarf that is smaller and cooler than the Sun. In addition to a Neptune-mass planet and a body of about eight Earth masses, a super-Earth that is about five times the mass of our planet also orbits Gliese 581. Labelled Gliese 581c, this body is thought to have a mean temperature of between zero and 40 degrees Celsius (32 to 104 degrees Fahrenheit) and a radius of about one-and-a-half times that of the Earth. Given these parameters, astronomers have speculated that Gliese 581c could harbour liquid water, either on a rocky

terrain or even in vast oceans. Further, the planet is predicted to reside in the 'habitable zone', a region around a star where the temperature conditions permit water to exist in liquid form. A conservative estimate of the current habitable zone of our Sun would be a fairly wide portion of the inner solar system: between 0.95 and 1.4 times the Earth-to-Sun distance.

The limit of habitability around a star will generally be affected by several factors. We will see shortly that the more massive stars evolve faster and have shorter lifetimes than less massive stars. If the total lifespan of a star falls below one billion years or so, this will significantly decrease the chances of life originating and becoming established upon it. Another factor affecting the potential for life is that massive stars emit substantial amounts of life-threatening ultraviolet radiation. Also relevant is the stability of the planet's orbit around its star. Planets with eccentric (as opposed to circular) orbits are more prone to collisions and extreme variations in physical conditions. We noted in *The Stellar Zoo, page 88*, that numerous stars in our Galaxy are in fact systems of two stars orbiting around each other. The gravitational interaction between stars in a binary system can certainly complicate the stability of the orbits of any planets present around either star.

As the number of known extra-solar planets increases, astronomers are able to study patterns in the properties of the host stars. One particular trend that stands out is that most of the exoplanets discovered so far are orbiting stars that have greater proportions of heavy chemical elements in their composition. Astronomers label all elements heavier than helium as 'metals'. The measurements of stellar properties raise the possibility that having a metal-rich star is an essential requisite for the formation of planets.

Recall that massive planets with rocky cores are thought to be forged over millions of years from material colliding and sticking together in a spinning disk of gas and dust that encircles the newborn star. A metal-rich star would have an abundance of heavier elements such as carbon, silicon and iron in its circumstellar disk. This factor makes it less likely for the disk material to be blown away by outflows from the infant star, thus promoting the gradual build up of planets. Indeed, surveys of hundreds of stars, some of which have been monitored over more than a decade, do provide evidence that stars that have

ABOVE: *To date, Earth is still the only planet known to harbour the biosignatures of life.*

RIGHT: *An illustration of a hot, Jupiter-like planet orbiting its parent star at less than 1 per cent of the distance between the Earth and the Sun.*

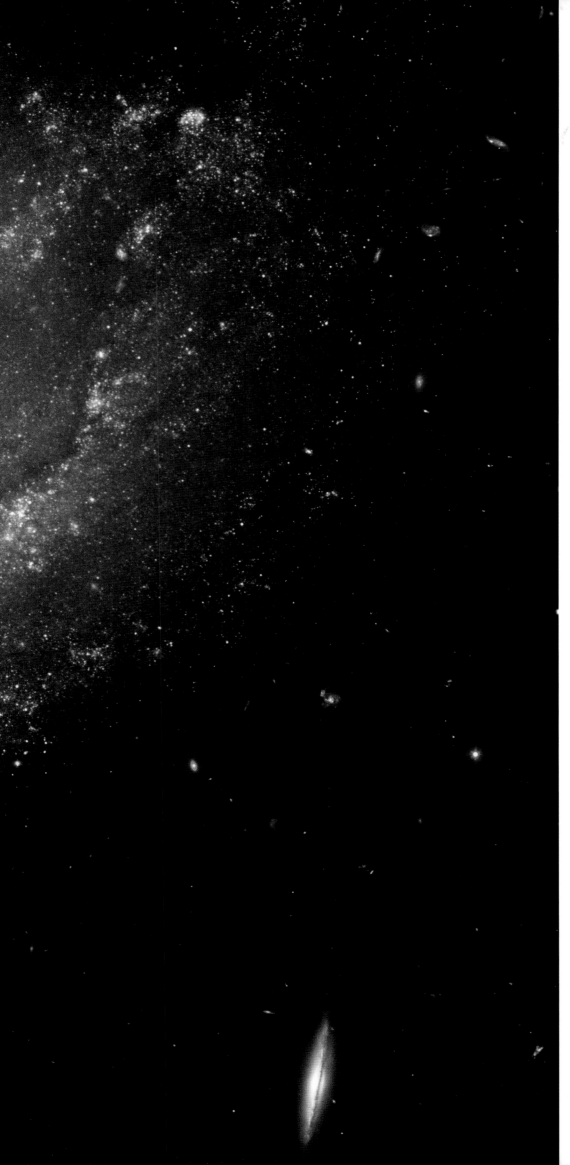

LEFT: The Galactic Habitable
Zones of spiral galaxies such
as NGC3370 are likely to host
numerous planetary systems.

the lowest percentage of iron, nickel, sodium, silicon and so on, have no detectable planets.

Stars in the solar neighbourhood suggest that our Sun is fairly metal-rich compared to other stars of its age and type. Some of this material may have been received by the Sun during its early evolution, perhaps as the polluted debris of smashed bodies that subsequently impacted into the surface of the star billions of years ago. From the viewpoint of habitable planets, it also helps that the Sun is not too massive, and has a favourable temperature and brightness. Further, the fact that it is essentially a solitary star allows stable near-circular orbits for planets like Earth. The possible link between the amount of metals in a star and its chance of hosting planets tells us the kinds of stars in the Milky Way Galaxy we need to focus on.

The structure of our Galaxy can be divided into four regions: the halo, the central bulge, the thick inner disk and the thin outer disk. The spiral arms of the Galaxy are sculpted into the inner and outer disk. Within these regions it is possible to identify a Galactic Habitable Zone, analogous to the Sun's habitable zone, where conditions are most favourable for not only the formation of planets, but also for life-forms to potentially thrive. Since heavy chemical elements are the building blocks for terrestrial planets and the cores of giant planets, the abundance of these elements is pivotal as to whether substantial planets can form.

The existence and quantities of these metals varies both among the stars and at different locations in our Galaxy. Old stars residing in a globular cluster in the halo of our Galaxy, for example, have barely 0.1 per cent of elements that are heavier than hydrogen and helium. Young stars in the disk of our Galaxy are more metal-rich, with a composition of perhaps about 2 per cent made up of heavier elements. However, even within the disk, the abundance of metals drops with distance away from the centre of the Galaxy. Conversely, regions of high metal content in the Galaxy close to the centre may lead to stars orbited by substantial numbers of giant planets which shift their orbital positions as they evolve. As these massive super-Jupiters migrate inward toward their host star, their gravitational influence would fling out smaller Earth-like bodies and eject them totally from the planetary system. There is therefore a 'Goldilocks zone' in the Galaxy, where the metal content of the stars and their circumstellar disks is high enough to form Earth-like planets, but low enough to prevent super-sized gas planets from destroying smaller terrestrial planets.

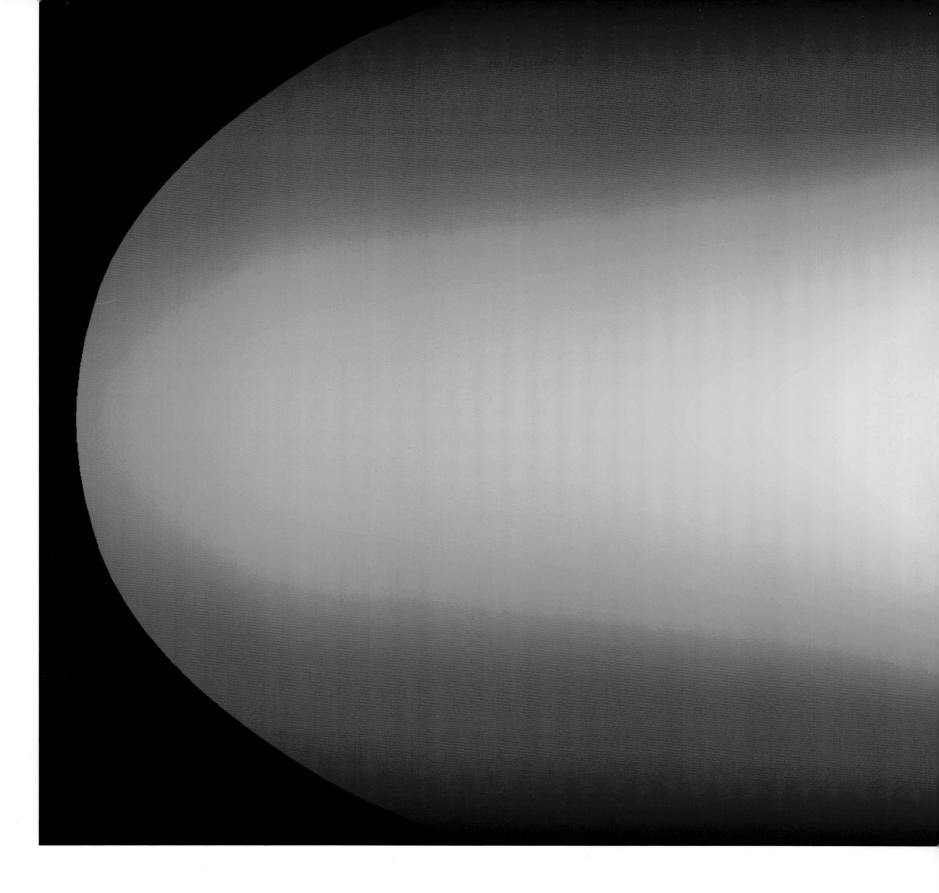

Another constraint in setting the boundaries for the habitable zone of our Galaxy comes from the hazards of exploding massive stars. The demise of the most massive stars results in violent supernovae explosions, and the blast waves from these final acts are accompanied by an enormous release of energy in the form of cosmic rays, X-rays and gamma rays. Intense doses of this radiation can be detrimental to life on Earth-like planets. Supernova explosions are more common in the densely packed, inner bulge regions of the Galaxy.

In effect, the combining factors of low metal content in the halo of our Galaxy and the high density of massive stars and frequent supernova explosions in the bulge and inner disk make these unlikely locations for numerous habitable terrestrial planets. The decreasing proportions of metals in the thin disk very far from the Galactic centre also places the outer regions of our Galaxy beyond the likely habitable zone. Models of the chemical composition of stars and their distribution suggest that the habitable zone of our Milky Way Galaxy is thus a fairly narrow

The first infrared map from the Spitzer Telescope of temperature changes across the upper cloud layer of an exoplanet known as HD189733b.

doughnut-like region that starts about 22,000 light-years from the centre and extends outward to 29,500 light-years. Surveys of stars residing in this annular region indicate that three-quarters of the objects found here are older than the Sun.

Of course, even once a terrestrial planet has formed in the prime locale of our Galaxy, numerous other factors could still affect its evolution and chances of supporting life forms. Our Sun, for example, enjoys a fairly stable orbit around the Galactic centre, which lowers the chances of

any glancing impacts with giant molecular clouds. Disturbances of this nature would stir up the reservoirs of comets that reside in the Oort cloud in the outer solar system, and expose the inner planets to fierce life-threatening cometary bombardments. A planet's atmosphere and magnetic field are important in shielding life-forms from the hazards of stellar radiation and maintaining a suitable temperature, while a stable climate is needed to permit complex life to evolve over an extended period of time.

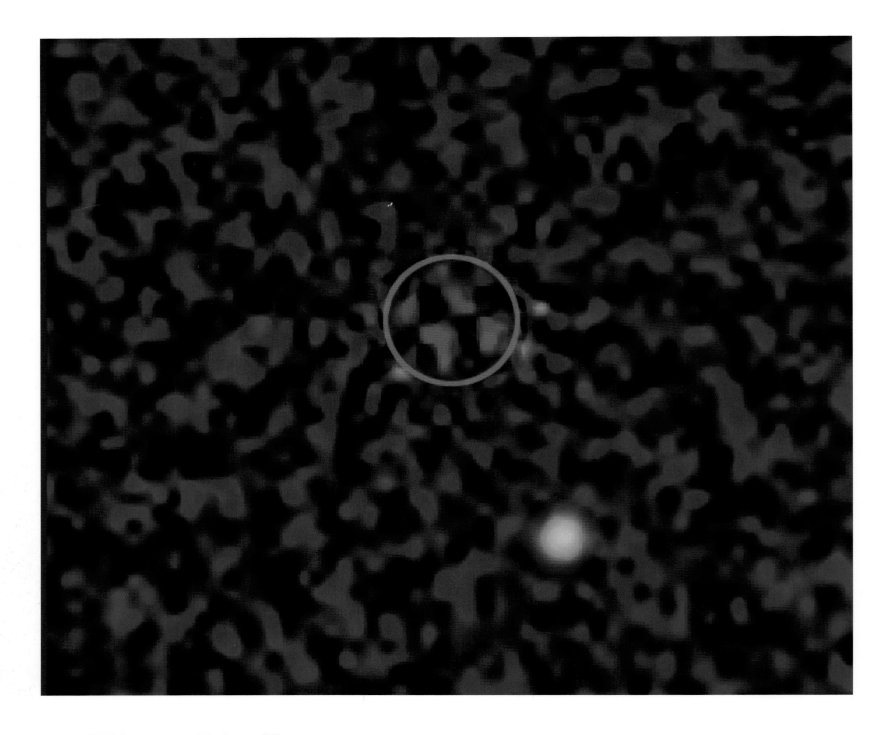

The Stellar Perspective

It is clear that an understanding of the nature of exoplanets demands in turn detailed studies of the properties of the host stars. Astrophysicists can derive physical properties of stars by analysing the emitted light through a spectrograph. The resulting spectra can be studied to reveal stellar quantities such as rotation rate, atmospheric conditions and the proportions of metals present. By building up a database on the characteristics of the planet-harbouring stars, it will become possible to answer questions as to whether the solar neighbourhood is significantly different from those of the other stars. We have already noted that the chances of finding a giant exoplanet increases for candidate stars of high metal content. This is a clear example of where an important relation exists between the nature of the host stars and their planets.

Another area of study involves the observation of direct interactions between the exoplanet and the star. Since the majority of exoplanets discovered so far are located extremely close to their stars, the bodies will interact gravitationally in different ways. It may turn out that the rate at which the star spins becomes synchronised with the time taken for the planet to complete one orbit, and could even lead to an increase in the spin rate of the star. Much

S Ori 52

S Ori 60

S Ori 56

Orion

like the Earth and Moon pairing, the very close-by giant planet could also induce bulges on a star. These might be evident as patches of much greater surface activity on the star, perhaps even magnetically connected and akin to the flares and eruptions seen on the Sun.

Aside from the growing interest in exploring solar-like stars, there is the scope of probing very young planets around newly-formed stars. At the other extreme, we can ask whether exoplanets can survive the ultimate demise of the host star, such as when it swells up into a red giant. Another perspective is that binary and multiple stellar systems are common in our Galaxy, but the stability of the proto-planetary disks and subsequent planet orbits are

likely to be more restricted in these cases. It might turn out, however, that planets in binary star systems offer critical clues as to how giant gas planets might form far away from a star and then migrate inward, to ultimately settle in the near-star locations that are apparent in so many of the exoplanet discoveries. Exploring the most diverse stellar settings will therefore help us to understand not only how planets form, but also their evolution.

LEFT: *Hubble Telescope detection of a 5-Jupiter-mass exoplanet candidate (bottom right). The glare of the brown dwarf host star (central ring) has been greatly reduced in processing the image.*

ABOVE: *Composite views of planet mass bodies discovered in star clusters at the heart of the Orion Nebula.*

Part three

VIOLENT DEATH

The Evolution and Demise of Stars

The stars that so gracefully mark out the familiar constellations in our night sky are not eternal. Each of these celestial markers will fade over billions of years; some will experience a comparatively passive demise, others will face a violent and explosive end. These final acts will not necessarily mean starless skies, however, as the birth of new stars is also expected to continue in our Galaxy for billions of years.

Our modern understanding of the lives and deaths of stars is based on extensive observations of numerous individual stars, which represent snapshots of the many different phases in their development. Somewhat like an archaeologist studying the bones of different ages, astronomers combine their observations to derive a sequence that tells a consistent story of how stars evolve over billions of years. The term 'stellar evolution' refers to the change over time of an individual star, which may be documented as changes in its temperature, size, mass and chemical composition.

Stars are not everlasting simply because they have a finite size, and therefore a limited supply of nuclear fuel. We noted earlier that the Sun, and indeed all stars, generates its energy to shine via nuclear fusion reactions that mostly occur in its core. The most efficient nuclear fusion process is the transmutation of hydrogen to helium, and stars spend the longest period of their lives in this phase.

After a few million years in formation, the Sun is currently about halfway through a 10-billion-year stage of producing energy through the fusion of hydrogen. This most stable period of a star's life is known as the 'main-sequence' phase. In addition to sustaining a star's luminous power output, the fusion energy source also provides the outward gas pressure to prevent the star from collapsing in on itself.

LEFT: *The Helix planetary nebula is constructed from matter ejected by a dying Sun-like star, almost 690 light-years away.*

The Battle Against Gravity

All stars in the Universe are locked in a life-long battle between the action of gravity trying to collapse the star, and the upward pressure of hot gas providing a counteracting push. Throughout most of its existence, a star is in balance, or equilibrium: an equal downward gravitational force matches the upward force from hot gas on each region, from the core to the surface. This means that if there is a drop in the amount of energy produced by nuclear reactions, gravity would take the upper hand and the star would start to contract. Conversely, should the core temperature rise, more energy would be released from the fusion reactions; this over-production would increase the gas pressure, thus making the star expand. During the stable phase of a star's life span, each internal layer will undergo adjustments to ensure that no excess force exists, and that equilibrium is maintained.

After many millions – or billions – of years in the stable, main-sequence phase, the hydrogen in the star's core will eventually have been fused entirely into helium. Initially at least, the core temperature will not be high enough to start fusing helium into a heavier element, so the 'fuel tank' will have become empty. This results in a substantial imbalance between the forces of gravity and gas pressure, resulting in the onset of relatively quick changes in the evolution of the star. With the gas pressure reduced, the core contracts under gravity, causing the gas temperature to rise (gravitational collapse always releases substantial energy). Depending on how massive the star is, it then becomes possible for further nuclear reactions to take place. For instance, when all of the hydrogen in the Sun's core has been used up and contraction begins, the core will heat up to a temperature of about 100 million degrees Celsius (180 million degrees Fahrenheit), which is sufficient to start a very brief phase of fusing helium nuclei into carbon. Some of the mass in this two-step reaction is converted into energy, and the star advances into the next phase of its pending demise.

At even higher core temperatures, the carbon nuclei can fuse with an additional helium nucleus to produce oxygen, and thus extract a little more energy. If sufficiently high temperatures can be reached in the stellar cores, it becomes possible for the end-products of one fusion stage to become the fuel for the next stage. In stars that are tens of times more massive than the Sun, successively heavier elements may be fused, such as oxygen into neon, followed by silicon and magnesium into a variety of nuclei from sulphur to iron. The final stages of the fusion of heavy elements are very short lived, however, perhaps only a few days from the ultimate stellar demise.

The formation of a core of iron marks the end of core energy production in massive stars, as iron fusion does not generate energy. The iron nucleus is the most strongly bound, and its fusion would absorb energy rather than release it. (Energy can only be extracted from elements heavier than iron via fission or splitting, such as is done with uranium in atomic weapons on Earth.) Toward the end of its life, a massive star will become a bloated supergiant, with a size comparable to Jupiter's orbit around Earth. The star will have an onion-skin-like structure on concentric layers made up of the ashes of several sequences of thermonuclear reactions. As we will see shortly, a very violent death then awaits the huge star.

RIGHT: A view of the globular cluster 47 Tuscane, revealing red giant stars among a dense grouping of almost 35,000 objects.

Birth Mass Matters

Whether or not the elements produced by fusion in one phase of a star's life will fuse in the next phase depends on how massive the star is. The most important factor that determines how a star evolves and dies is its mass at birth. The most massive stars have shorter lifetimes of perhaps a few tens of millions of years compared to less massive stars, such as the Sun, which have a life span of more than 10 billion years. This concept can be understood by remembering that a stable star needs to maintain a balance between the collapsing force of gravity and the outward counteraction provided by the pressure from hot gas in the interior. More massive stars will have a stronger gravity, thus requiring higher interior temperature to provide a greater outward pressure. However, at higher temperatures the nuclear fusion process runs faster, which then generates greater luminous power. This means that the massive star will use up its supply of nuclear fuel more quickly, and will thus have a shorter life. In short, the life span of a star depends on the ratio of its mass (or fuel supply) and the rate at which it is consuming the fuel.

As we have seen, the different stages through which a star evolves, the nature of its demise and the object left as a remnant all depend on the initial mass of the star at the time of its formation. We can crudely borrow from the world of boxing the categories of lightweight, middleweight and heavyweight to follow the different evolution scenarios. Lightweight stars, such as the Sun, are those born with masses in the range between about one and eight times the Sun's mass. These stars will spend about 10 billion years in their stable main-sequence phase of hydrogen fusion, and then evolve into red giant stars. Their end-state will be a compact, Earth-sized star of up to about one times the Sun's mass, known as 'white dwarfs'. The formation of a white dwarf remnant is preceded by the relatively gentle ejection of the star's outer layers to form an object known as a planetary nebula.

Middleweight stars have an initial mass of between eight and twenty-five solar masses. Following a shorter main-sequence phase of tens of millions of years, these more massive stars will quickly pass though a red giant phase and undergo a supernova explosion once all nuclear energy production has come to an end. The remnant left after this disintegration is a very exotic, city-sized, neutron star.

The heavyweight stars will have birth masses of about 25 to 100 times that of the Sun. These are the most rapidly evolving stellar objects, spending barely a few million years in the hydrogen fusion phase. Their demise is initially marked by their ballooning into supergiant stars that then explode as supernovae. The end-state of these stars is a black hole of perhaps a few solar masses.

LEFT: *Striking Hubble Telescope image of the star V838 Mon, which has previously ejected layers of gas from its outer regions.*

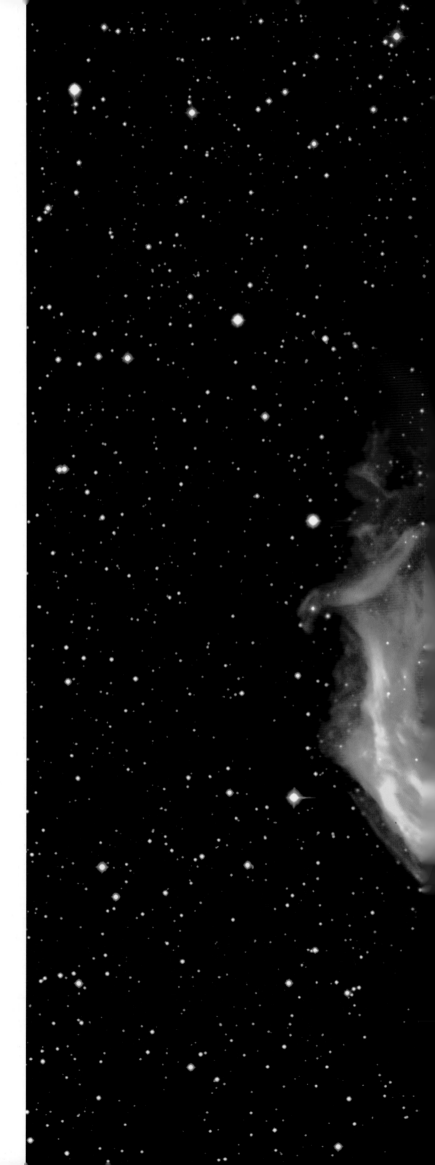

The Fate of the Sun

Out of the almost 200 billion stars that make up our spiral-shaped Milky Way Galaxy, almost one third are Sun-like in their size and surface temperatures. These relatively 'lightweight' stars will share similar histories, acted out over 10 billion years or so. The Sun will spend most of its lifetime fusing hydrogen to helium, and thus maintaining the energy output to keep itself stable. Astronomers estimate that the Sun's fuel tank is now half empty, and the remaining hydrogen in the core will have been depleted in another five billion years. The Sun's internal balance will then start to alter and its appearance will change quickly as it moves out of the extended main-sequence phase.

With the central solar engine no longer providing energy, the self-gravity of the vast, gaseous ball will gain the upper-hand and start to compress down on the core, which at that stage will be composed of helium. The squeezing of the helium core will convert gravitational energy to raise the central temperature and heat up the immediately surrounding layers of gas. Over millions of years, the density of the core will have risen to around 100 million kilograms per cubic metre, and temperatures will have soared to 100 million degrees Celsius (180 million degrees Fahrenheit). In these fierce conditions, it will become possible for the central engine of the Sun to reignite and begin reactions to fuse helium into carbon. This will be only a brief 'second wind' of energy, however, somewhat like a car driver squeezing an extra litre of petrol from a small reserve tank.

The compression and turmoil occurring in the inner regions of the Sun in crisis lies in contrast with the more gentle changes occurring to its outermost layers. The extra energy extracted from the helium fusion reactions, together with a last-ditch fusion of hydrogen in a thin ring immediately around the core, will cause layers of gas beyond the core to expand. Through a series of unstable swellings, the Sun will bloat outward until its radius is about 30 times greater than it is today. This phase in the life of Sun-like stars is known as the 'red giant' phase. There are numerous examples of stars in the sky that have already reached this retirement age, such as Arcturus in the constellation of Boötes and Aldebaran in Taurus. These

RIGHT: *Layers of ejected gas and dust surround the dying Sun-like star Sharpless 2–188, located 2,800 light-years from Earth.*

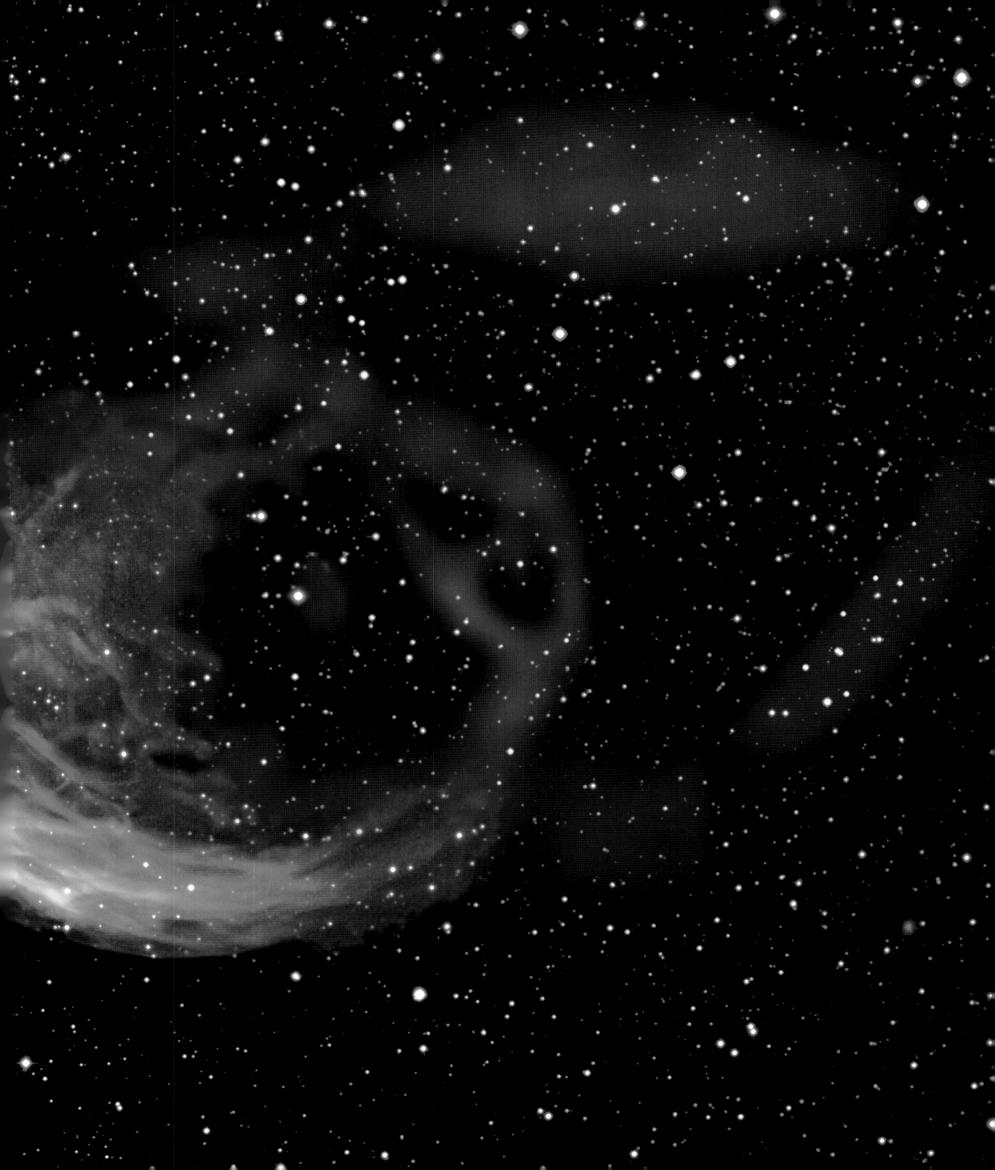

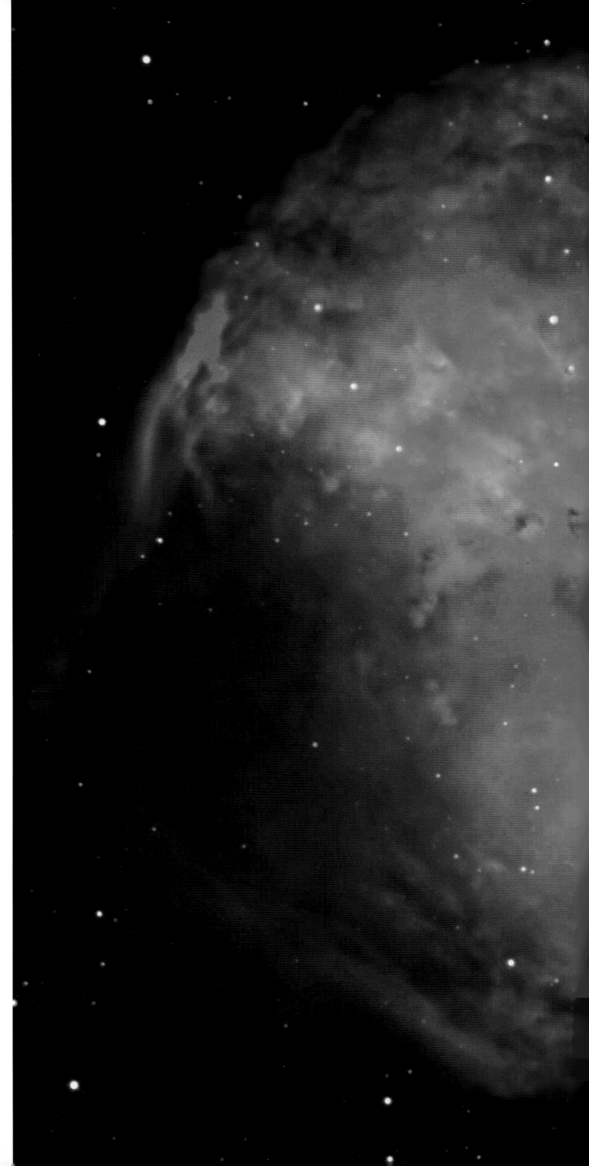

stars have a reddish appearance because as they expand their outer layers move further away from the hot core and thus cool down. The exterior or surface temperature drops to around 3,000 degrees Celsius (5,700 degrees Fahrenheit), and the light emitted has a red hue.

The ballooning of the Sun into a red giant begs the question: what will happen to the Earth? The gradual demise of the Sun over the next five billion years will have grave consequences for our planet and its neighbouring rocky partners. Indeed, the Earth is predicted to face a grim solar furnace two billion years hence, and well before the Sun turns into a red giant. By studying the lives of other Sun-like stars and making sophisticated model predictions using powerful computers, astronomers believe that the Sun will get hotter and brighter on its way to evolving into a red giant. The Sun is, for example, already 20 per cent brighter today than it was when the Earth formed about 4,500 million years ago.

A more luminous Sun will cause the temperature of the Earth to rise, and more water will evaporate from the oceans. These events will, in turn, lead to more carbon dioxide being washed out of the atmosphere by increased rainfall. A billion years from now, the average temperature on our planet could exceed 50 degrees Celsius (120 degrees Fahrenheit), and reach close to 100 degrees Celsius (210 degrees Fahrenheit) a few hundred million years after that. There would be no carbon dioxide left in the atmosphere to regulate the Earth's temperature, and all life, including the hardiest microbes, will have died out. In three billion years all of the Earth's oceans will have evaporated, leaving a sterile planet. Prolific volcanoes would now inject a new source of carbon dioxide into a rainless atmosphere, thus allowing its concentration to rise rapidly. The effect will be to create a runaway greenhouse effect on an already scorched planet, raising the temperature further to a sizzling 250 degrees Celsius (480 degrees Fahrenheit). Our once lush green, brown and blue planet will now resemble what the harsh planet Venus looks like today.

The devastation on Earth may already be global, but two billion years later it will still have to face the fury of the Sun as a red giant star. The Sun will have expanded out to a radius of almost 170 million kilometres (105 million miles). Mercury, the innermost planet, will be rapidly swallowed. Venus is also predicted not to escape the solar swelling, and will find itself nearly 30 million kilometres (18 million miles) below the red giant Sun's surface.

Precisely what will happen to the Earth will depend on how much of its own mass the Sun loses during this unstable phase. The study of Sun-like stars that have already evolved into red giants suggests that the Sun could

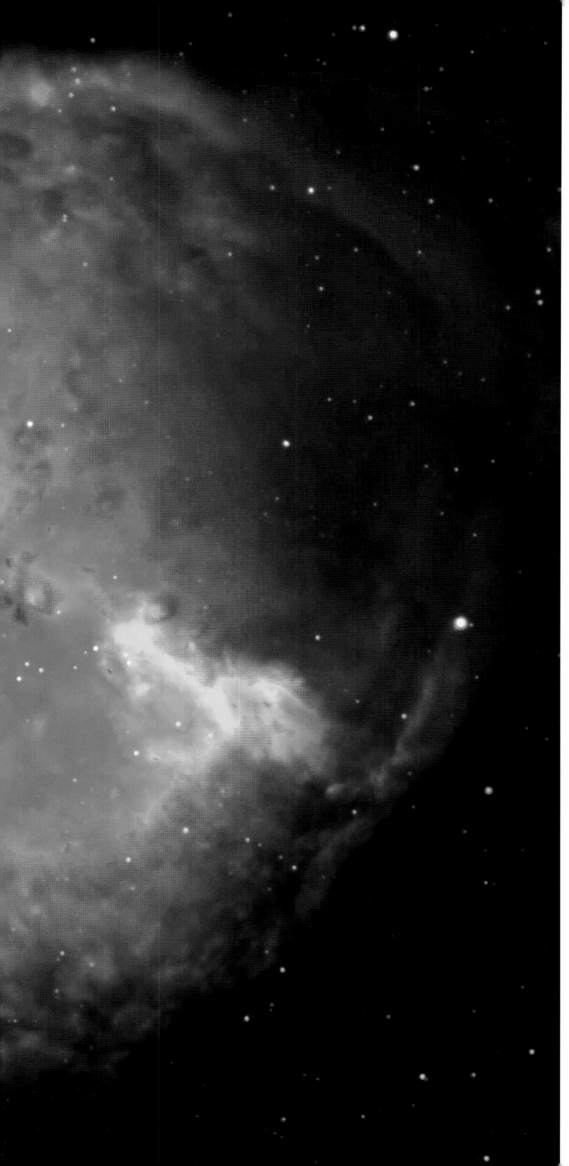

lose up to 20 per cent of its present mass. These stars eject matter through powerful winds and large shells of material. If the Sun does indeed shed this amount of matter, then its lower mass will cause it to have a weaker gravitational pull on the planets, with the result that the orbits of the planets will migrate outward. In the case of the Earth, our planet may move out by 35 million kilometres (21 million miles) from its present position to 185 million kilometres (115 million miles) from the centre of the Sun. This 'trick' means that the Earth would narrowly escape the expected reach of the fully bloated Sun. However, the amount of mass the Sun will shed is still debated by scientists, and certainly if the Earth stays roughly in today's orbit, it will be truly consumed. Even if the Earth's orbit shifts out to escape being gobbled, the red giant Sun will appear huge and cover almost half of the sky. The temperature on Earth will have soared to several hundred thousand degrees, and daylight would be 3,000 times brighter than it is now.

It is clear, then, that if our human civilization is to evolve into a truly long-lived race its survival will depend on figuring out how to migrate away from Earth over the next billion years or so.

LEFT: *Ground-based optical image of the Dumbbell planetary nebula, which signals the death of a Sun-like star more than 1,200 light-years from Earth.*

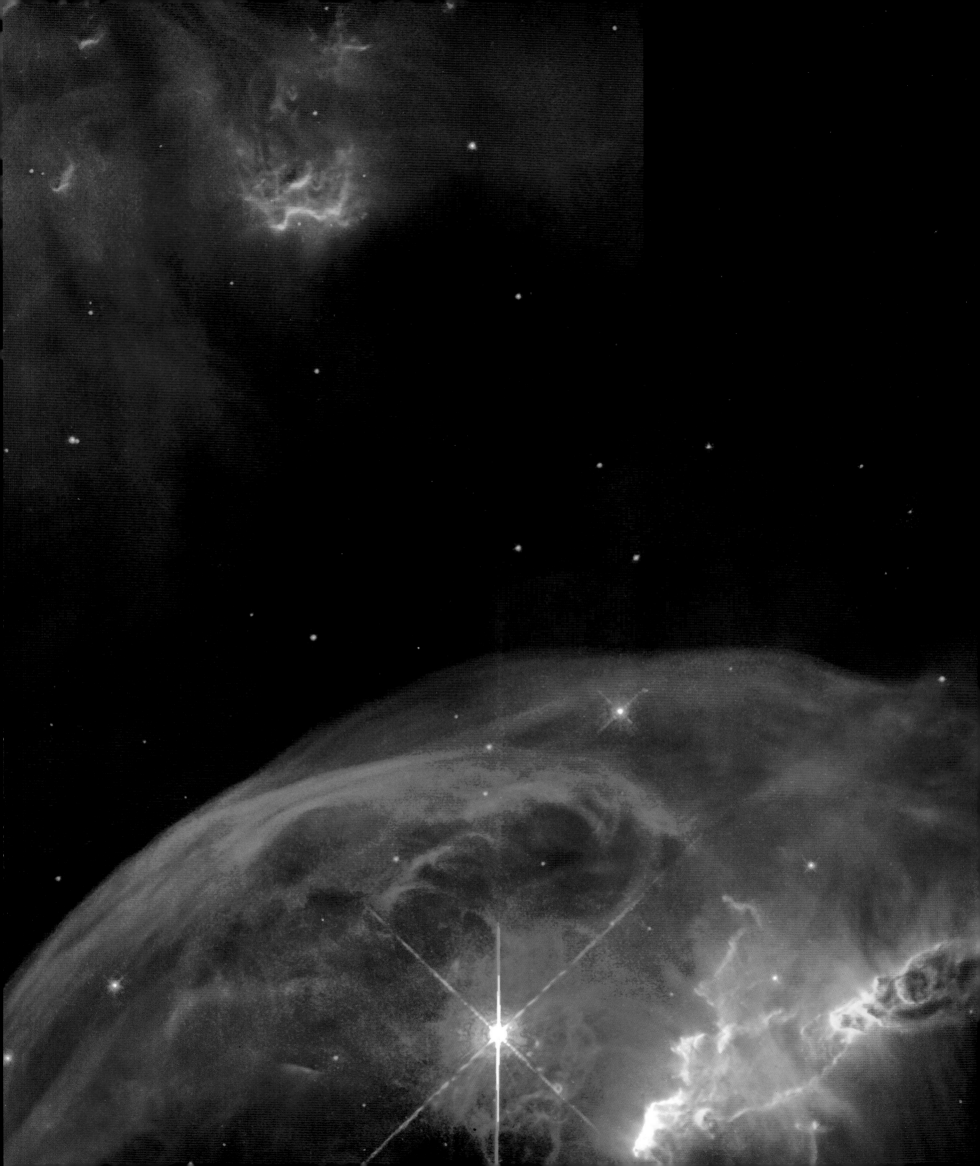

BELOW: *Powerful outflows of gas from a star helped to sculpt this spherical bubble of hot matter, about 7,100 light-years from Earth.*

A Stunning End

Ironically, the final phase in the death of Sun-like stars results in one of the most spectacular and colourful objects in the Universe. The 'red giant' stage lasts about 2 billion years, after which time the end-state of the Sun becomes very imminent. As the Sun exhausts all of its hydrogen and helium fuel, it desperately starts to rearrange its inner regions. After the helium fusion phase is complete, an inner core of carbon forms. The central engine cuts out once more, however, and gravity starts to pull the core inwards. The temperature rises again, causing the remnant thin layers of helium that surround the core to briefly fuse and generate additional heat. The Sun will then swell for a second time to enter another red giant phase. Stars like the Sun are not massive enough to raise the core temperature to the 600 million degrees Celsius (1000 million degrees Fahrenheit) temperature needed to initiate substantial carbon fusion reactions. The formation of a carbon core will thus mark the exhaustion of nuclear energy generation in the Sun.

With all nuclear reactions now ceased, our star is barely able to hold itself together any longer. The outer layers are freed from the gravitational pull of the core and get puffed out into space like giant smoke rings. Over a period of 10,000 years or so, these layers of gas will spread out over vast distances to form a striking object known as a 'planetary nebula'. These intricate bubble-like structures can be up to three light-years across, and carry away certain life-giving chemicals made inside the Sun, such as carbon. (Note that the name 'planetary nebula' has nothing at all to do with planets; the name was given in the early 19th century, when such objects appeared as fuzzy planet-like bodies when viewed through the telescopes of that time.)

Planetary nebulae are glowing shells of gas that are ejected by low-mass stars near the end of their lives. Almost 1,500 have been discovered so far in our Milky Way Galaxy, and it is estimated that up to 50,000 more are currently hidden away behind interstellar clouds of gas and dust. Several planetary nebulae have been imaged in exquisite detail by the Hubble Space Telescope and other observatories. One of the nearest planetary nebulae currently on view lies about 650 light-years away in the direction of the constellation of Aquarius. Known as the Helix Nebula, the ejected outer layers of a dying star are seen in vivid colours as the material basks in intense ultraviolet radiation from the surviving stellar core.

The main rings of matter in the Helix Nebula span a diameter of almost one-and-a-half light-years, and were

expelled between 6,000 and 12,000 years ago. The overall circular appearance of the Helix does not appear as such because the nebula is shaped like a ball, but rather because we are viewing one end of a vast cylinder of glowing gases. Detailed telescopic images have revealed spoke-like features that are incorporated within the colourful shells of gas. Each of these numerous spoke-like structures has a head that is twice the size of our solar system, and each has a tail, which points away

from the remnant hot central star. These tentacle-like features may have formed when fast-moving hot gas crashed into cooler and denser shells of material that were ejected at an earlier time.

Observations made in the infrared waveband with the Spitzer Space Telescope have also revealed the presence of dust circling in the outer regions of the Helix Nebula. The dust is thought to be relatively fresh in origin, perhaps formed due to frantic collisions between comets at the

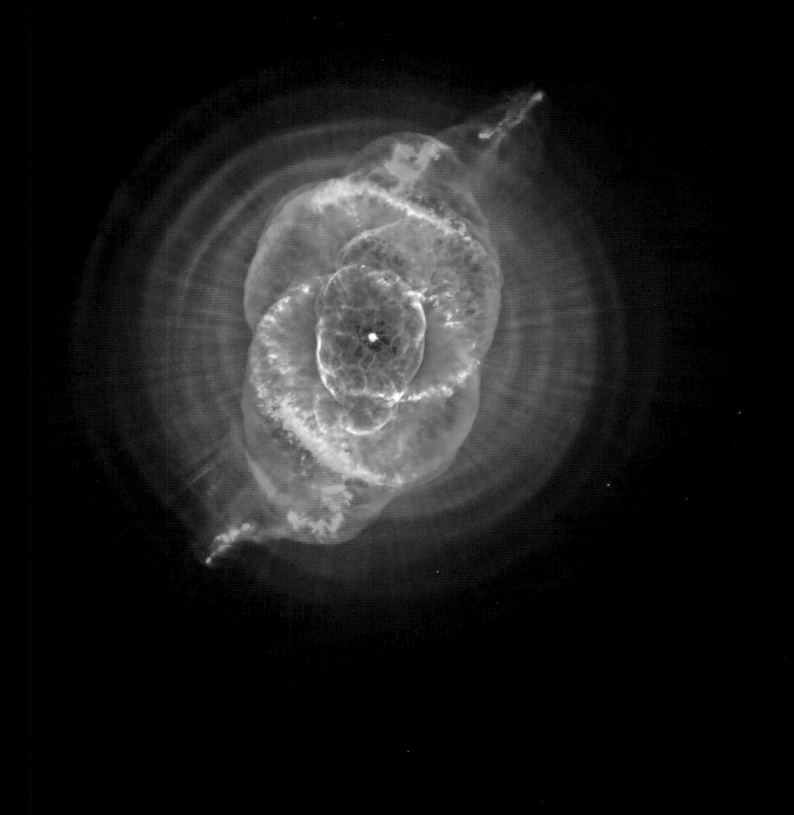

fringe of the nebula. Millions of years earlier, prior to the ejection of the nebular material, the Sun-like star may have been orbited by planets and comets. Following its demise via a red giant phase, the planets were perhaps swallowed as the star bloated out, while comets and asteroids much further out would have been vigorously stirred up by the extensive structural changes occurring in the inner regions.

Another stunning example of a planetary nebula is the so-called Cat's Eye Nebula, seen toward the constellation of Draco. Concentric shells, or bubbles of gas, have been ejected as the Sun-like star approached its demise, about 3,600 light-years from Earth. More than a dozen nested shells, each ejected over intervals of about 1,500 years, interact with jets of high-speed gas coming from the hot, compact white dwarf star that remains at the centre of the Cat's Eye. Additionally, knots of gas are mixed in, which arise as different regions slam into each other and create shock waves. These remarkable interactions account for

ABOVE: *The complex Cat's Eye planetary nebula, imaged at a distance of about 3,000 light-years.*

the very intricate and complex morphology of this planetary nebula, which has been revealed to us in great detail by the Hubble Space Telescope.

The various patterns evident in the nebula provide direct clues as to how Sun-like stars shed mass as they approach the end of their lives. Astronomers are seeking to understand, for example, why the ejections have taken place over regular intervals. One explanation might be that these intervals are related to cycles in the magnetic activity of the star, or perhaps they betray pulses at the stellar surface. Such revealing imagery of the nebula provides us with a 'fossil record' of the final phases leading up to the death of a star.

Given that stars are vast, spherical-shaped gaseous objects, it is reasonable to suppose that the structures formed when they puff away their outer layers would also consist of large spheres. Telescopic images have revealed, however, that only a minority of planetary nebulae have roughly spherical shapes. More than half of the known planetary nebulae exhibit considerably more complex morphologies, thus raising puzzling questions as to how they form.

An intriguing example is the object called Mz3 in the constellation of Norma. This nebula has been dubbed 'Ant Nebula' since its shape resembles the head and thorax of an ant. Gas is expelled from the dying star at speeds of 1,000 kilometres per second (620 miles per second) to form a light-year-long structure that is extensively embedded with knots and clumps of gas. Overall, Mz3 exhibits a high degree of symmetry in the two main lobes blown away in opposite directions from the compact central object left behind. One possible explanation for the non-spherical appearance of the nebula is that the central star may in fact be a binary system. The interaction between the two stars would then result in a more elongated and non-spherical nebula. Another possibility is that the dying star is spinning very quickly, and has a strong magnetic field that gets wound up to a very high degree. Material is then accelerated along the twisted magnetic field lines in more confined directions.

The imagery from powerful telescopes has revealed that many planetary nebulae have rather complex shapes. The variety on view ranges from donut-shaped structures, plate-like disks and nested bubbles to blobs, jet streams, pinwheel patterns and hourglass shapes. The reasons for this rich variety are not fully understood. In some cases, as in Mz3, there may be gravitational interactions between pairs of central stars. A companion star may act to increase the spin rate of a bloated red giant that is advancing to its demise. The increased rotation speed of the red giant may then lead to much more confined, jet-like outflows which ultimately help to shape a non-spherical nebula. It is even possible for the dying star's system of planets to alter the flow of material as the nebula forms, thus resulting in more complex and chaotic-appearing shapes. A deeper understanding of how different nebula shapes arise will ultimately help us to predict what type of planetary nebula will be puffed out by our Sun, and how it will interact with the terrestrial and giant planets in our solar system.

Over a period of about 20,000 years, the fluorescent light from our Sun's planetary nebula will fade away as the expelled gases expand, cool and eventually disperse into the interstellar medium that is sparsely distributed between the stars. The tombstone left behind will be a bare core of highly compressed carbon, known as a white dwarf star, and this is where the story of the Sun's life finally ends. Having been squeezed into a planet-sized ball, the initially very hot cinder will gradually cool as it radiates, somewhat like a piece of hot coal. Over billions of years, the Sun will then slowly turn from a hot, white dwarf star to a cold, dark and undetectable relic, taking a possible still surviving planet Earth into a deep freeze with it.

RIGHT: *Composite X-ray, optical and infrared images of varied planetary nebulae, including the 'Ant Nebula' Mz3 (main upper image).*

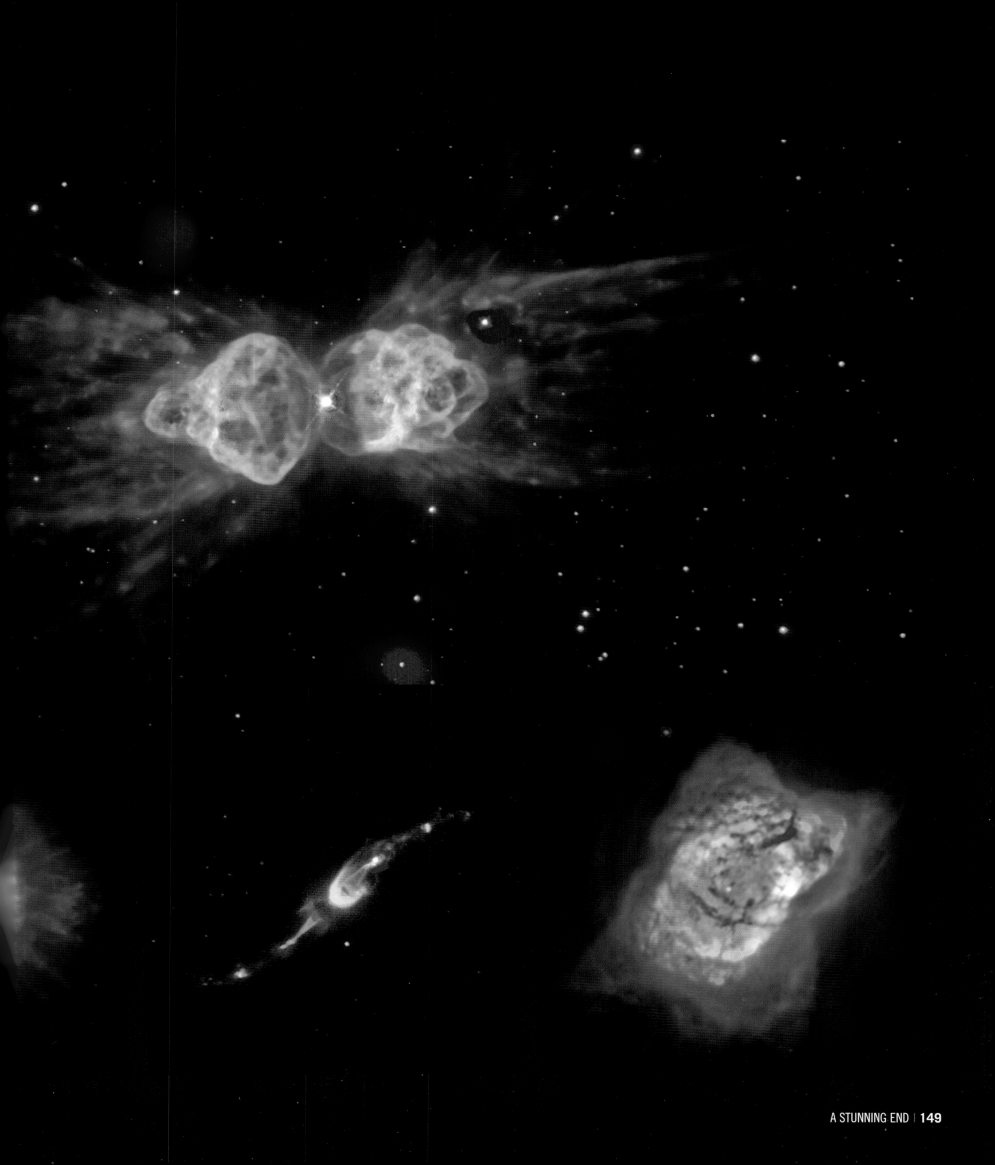

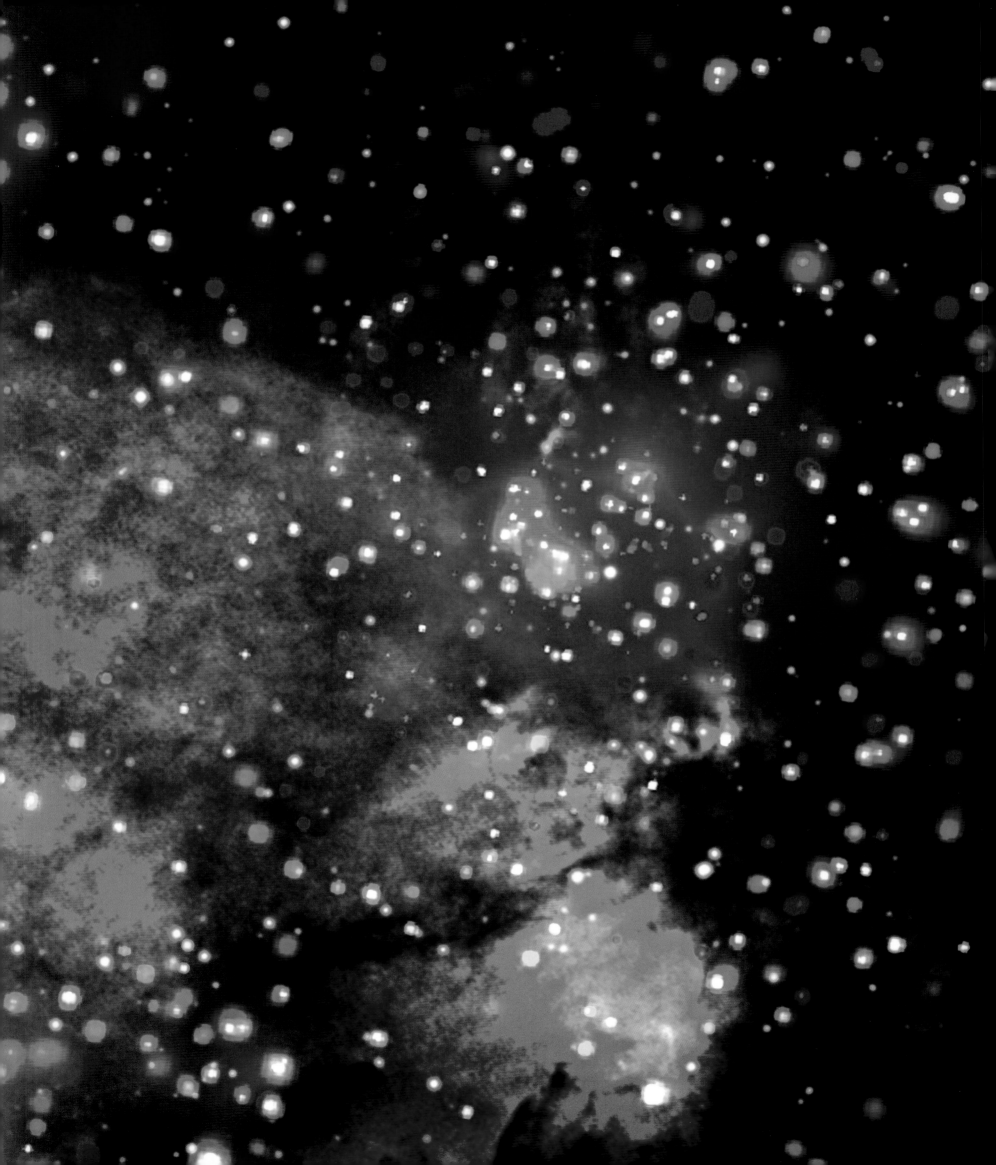

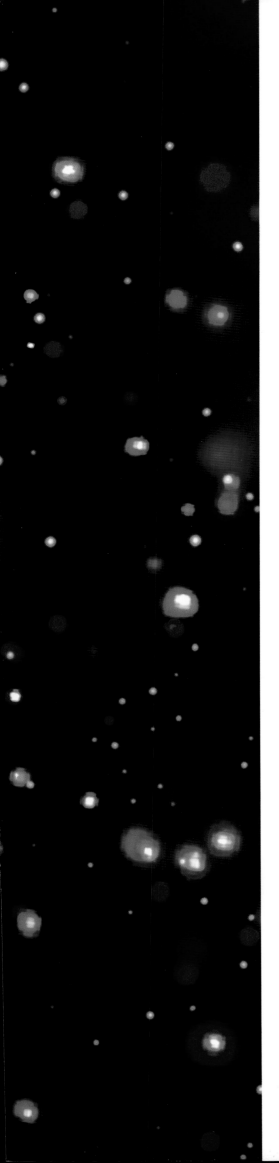

Doomed Massive Stars

Stars forming in our Galaxy today can have masses ranging from about a tenth of a solar mass to more than 100 times the mass of the Sun. However, the star-making process favours the creation of low-mass stars, and thus there are considerably more stars in our Galaxy with a birth mass less than that of the Sun than there are high mass stars. Though few in numbers, massive stars do nevertheless have a tremendous influence on their galaxies. High-mass stars of tens of solar masses can be thousands or millions of times more luminous than the Sun, thus radiating prolific amounts of energy. Additionally, massive stars have prodigious stellar winds that inject nuclear-processed material into the surrounding interstellar medium. The most luminous stars can lose material equivalent to the Sun's total mass over a few hundred thousand years, a relatively short time span. Such high rates of mass loss through stellar winds can even affect the manner in which the star evolves.

We have already noted that birth mass is a pivotal parameter that determines not only a star's power output and size, but also the manner of its demise and ultimate fate. Massive stars lose the inexorable battle against the crushing force of gravity in the most spectacular fashion. The nuclear reactions in their cores proceed at a greater rate than in Sun-like stars, to provide the high gas pressures needed to counter the vast weight of the outer regions of the star pushing down. Thus, not only do massive stars radiate more energy, they also use up their internal fuel supplies at a much quicker rate. For example, a star that is ten times the Sun's mass will complete its life cycle almost 300 times faster than the Sun. The stable main-sequence phase, during which hydrogen in the core is fused to helium, will barely last three million years for a star that is 60 times the mass of the Sun, compared with the ten billion years the Sun spends in this evolutionary stage.

LEFT: *Chandra false-colour X-ray image of a 6,000-light-year distant cluster of massive stars known as M3.*

The Elements of Life

Since the core temperatures of massive stars get extremely high, it becomes possible for these stars to undergo sequentially more advanced nuclear fusion stages, thus producing heavier chemical products. In the early stages of the Big Bang origin of the Universe, only the lightest few elements were formed. Following the cosmic creation of hydrogen, the Universe was initially hot enough to then fuse protons to make helium, in a similar way to the nuclear reactions that occur within the cores of stars. Very sparse amounts of lithium and beryllium were also formed at these earliest epochs.

As the Universe expanded it became too cool for the fusion of helium into heavier elements. All of the other chemical elements that we know of were assembled at a much later time, inside stars and during supernova explosions. The cores of the Sun-like stars can only attain high enough temperatures and pressures to make abundant amounts of helium and, subsequently, carbon. The creation of most elements that are heavier than carbon is only possible within the interiors of massive stars; this includes the fusion of atomic nuclei to create oxygen, neon, sodium, magnesium, silicon and iron. Massive stars are thus responsible for the origin of the chemical elements needed for life, as these elements were not made during the Big Bang.

In the late stages of evolution, massive stars eject these 'seeds' of life throughout interstellar space via powerful stellar winds, unstable ejections of the outer layers and, finally, as supernovae explosions. The ashes of ancient supernovae explosions drifted across vast distances to inseminate our proto-planetary nebula with the fundamental building blocks of life. Almost five billion years ago, this now chemically rich nebula began to collapse under its own gravity to form the Sun and the other bodies in our solar system, including an Earth that was to become biologically thriving. Our lives and those of massive stars are thus inextricably linked.

After a relatively rapid main-sequence phase, massive stars enter a red giant or supergiant phase, whereby they balloon up to enormous sizes and have an internal

RIGHT: *Ground-based image of the vast star-forming Carina Nebula, which also hosts the powerful star eta Carinae (near image centre).*

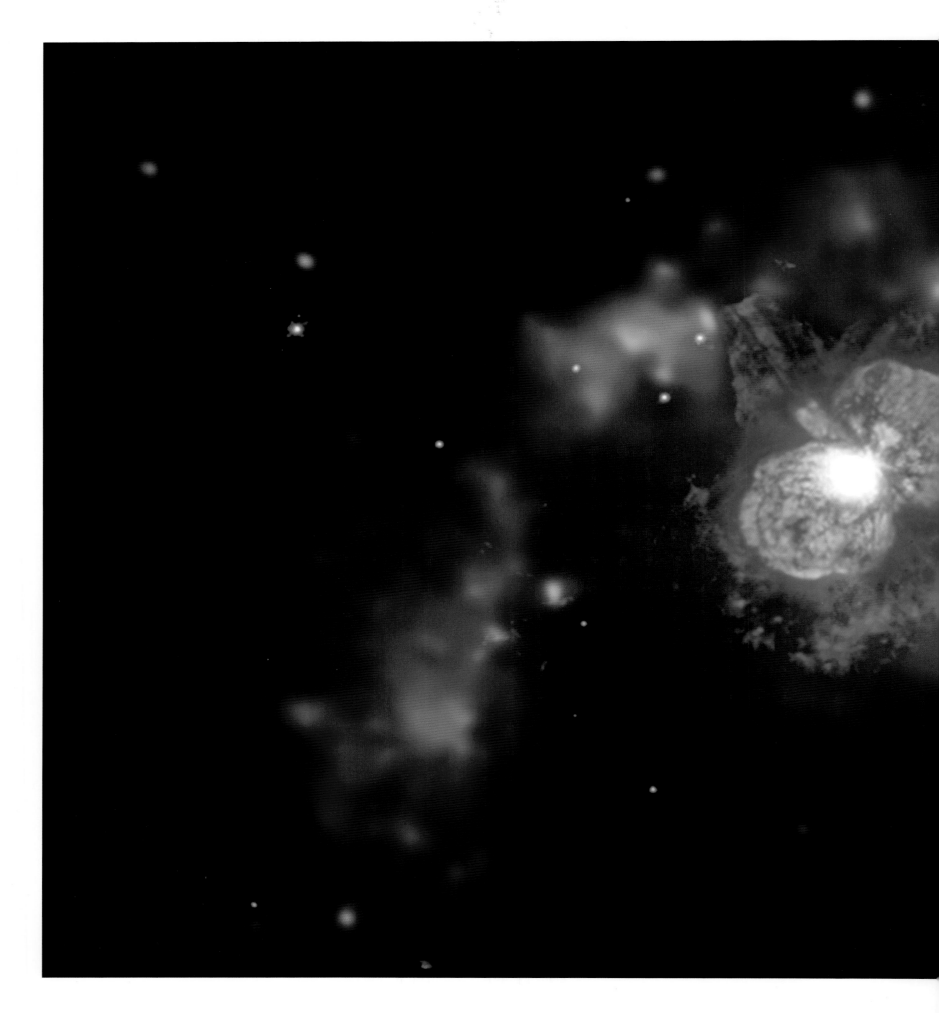

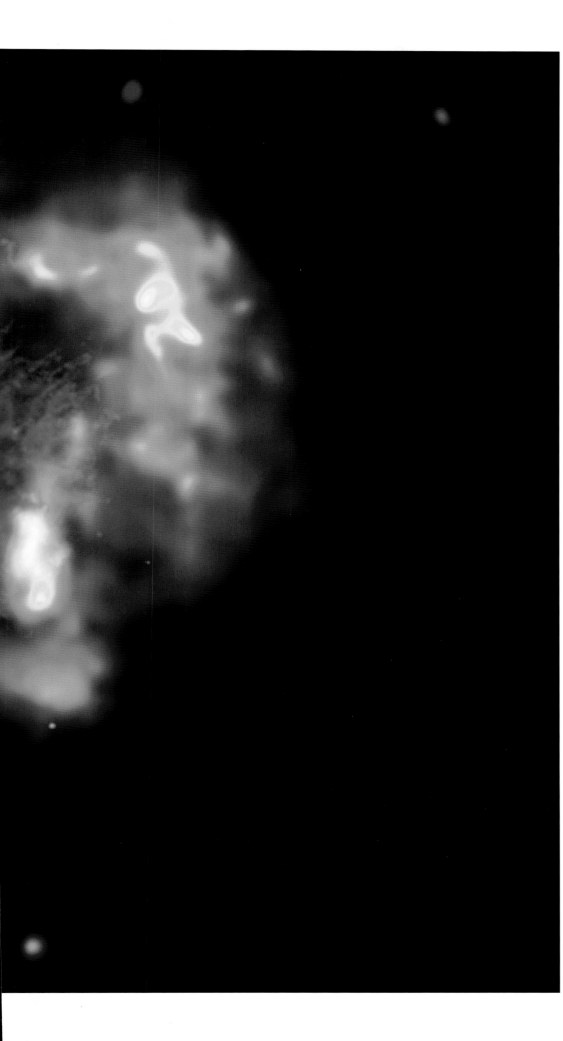

structure made up of concentric shells. Each shell or layer is cooler and less dense than the one further in. The impending and catastrophic doom may be preceded by frantic adjustments of the star, as it starts to become highly unstable against the relentless force of gravity.

One of the most massive stars in our Galaxy is currently in this critical stage of its life. About 7,500 light-years distant from Earth and toward the constellation of Carina, Eta Carinae is a remarkable star that is rapidly nearing its final phases. This enigmatic and massive object dramatically increased in brightness between 1837 and 1856, when it became the second brightest star in the night sky, outshone only by Sirius. Known as the 'Great Eruption', Eta Carinae ejected a pair of huge, billowing clouds of gas and dust, which have been viewed in astounding detail by the Hubble Space Telescope and the Chandra X-ray telescope. Material amounting to about four times the mass of the Sun was expelled, and even today the ejecta is still expanding out at speeds of up to 650 kilometres per second (400 miles per second). Hubble images revealed lobes of clumpy and turbulent matter, separated by a central plate-like disk in the equatorial plane of the star. Streaks and spokes are also seen sculpted into the expanding clouds, some of which are up to half a light-year long.

Eta Carinae remains variable today, exhibiting regular changes in its light output over a five-and-a-half-year cycle. The repeating pattern of fluctuations in the visual, X-ray and radio wavebands raises the possibility that the central massive star is being orbited by a companion star. The main star in Eta Carinae is almost four million times brighter than the Sun, making it one of the most powerful stars known. This incredible luminosity implies that the primary star has a mass of at least 100 times that of the Sun. Eta Carinae will have a comparatively short life span of no more than three million years. Given its relatively nearby location in our Galaxy, its final demise is likely to present a spectacular sight in our skies.

Possibly one of the most intrinsically brightest stars in our Galaxy is known as the Pistol Star. Its name comes from the fact that it is surrounding a pistol-shaped nebula that contains more than ten Sun masses of ejected material. This star is about 25,000 light-years away from us, toward the direction of the Galactic centre. This

LEFT: *Composite optical (inner region) and X-ray images of the highly unstable, massive star eta Carinae, which is 7,500 light-years from Earth.*

massive star in turmoil has a power output that is ten million times greater than the Sun. This extreme power output suggests that its current mass is at least 80 times that of the Sun, and that it was probably born about 150 times more massive than the Sun between one to three million years ago. The Pistol Star is predicted to undergo a spectacular supernova explosion over the next two million years or so.

The most massive star currently known is the brightest hot star seen in a young cluster called NGC3603. The star, which is 20,000 light-years distant from Earth, is simply named A1, and is estimated to be 114 times the mass of the Sun. The mass of A1 can be reliably determined because it is part of a binary star system, and thus its orbit can be measured. Even its companion star is estimated to be at least 80 solar masses.

Our current understanding of the structure of stars in galaxies such as ours is that they have a maximum birth mass limit of 150 times the Sun's mass. This limit arises because as the star gets increasingly massive, the pressure pushing outwards to keep the star stable actually becomes overwhelming. The intense radiation of very massive stars pushes extremely strongly outwards, and exceeds the force of gravity pulling inward. This means that stars forming today that are in excess of 150 times the Sun's mass would never be stable.

It is possible, however, that the first stars created in the very early stages of the Universe could have exceeded 150 Sun masses, and may even have been several hundred times more massive. The reason for the size of these 'first generation' stars is that they were assembled from only the pristine light elements: hydrogen and helium. The lack of heavy chemical elements at the earliest epoch meant that the stars had reduced outward pressures compared to massive stars that formed billions of years later.

RIGHT: *Spitzer Telescope infrared view toward the centre of our Galaxy, revealing supernova remnants amidst vast glowing regions of interstellar gas and dark dust.*

Supernovae

After a comparatively short life span, the core of a massive star will eventually be composed mostly of iron, thus marking the end of fusion energy production. The most violent of fates then awaits the star. With no outward gas pressure to withstand the action of gravity, the vast star, with its extended outer layers, collapses down rapidly onto the iron core. Millions of years of stellar evolution are undone in barely a few seconds.

During this phenomenal gravitational collapse, the temperature in the core rises to exceed 100 billion degrees Celsius (212 billion Fahrenheit), crushing the iron atoms together. An enormous amount of energy is released as the implosion rebounds off the hard, highly-compressed core. The resultant recoil produces a violent outward-moving shock wave that explodes at almost 15,000 kilometres per second (9,300 miles per second). Over a period of a few hours, the outer layers of the star are blasted well away from the core. Somewhat like a rapidly expanding fireball, huge amounts of nuclear-processed material are propelled into space, including the building blocks of life. This ejecta of hot gas will ultimately cool and spread into the interstellar medium, possibly to be incorporated into the formation of the next generation of stars. The aftermath of a supernova explosion is known as a supernova remnant.

A supernova explosion can release tremendous amounts of energy, and can briefly shine with the equivalent brightness of ten billion Suns. A substantial fraction of the total energy of a supernova is not emitted as electromagnetic radiation, but rather is carried out by exotic neutrino particles, similar to those discussed earlier in this book in the context of the Sun's core reactions (*see pages 104–105*). The brilliance of supernovae means that they can be readily detected in other galaxies, and thus they act as true beacons of the Universe.

Supernovae are very rarely seen in our Milky Way Galaxy (even though it is estimated that one occurs about once every hundred years) because these explosions mostly happen in very distant parts of the Galaxy, where they remain obscured from our telescopes by the vast regions of gas and dust that pervade the space between stars. The detection of supernovae is of great importance in understanding the final stages of stellar destruction.

Supernovae observed in our Galaxy in the past include those discovered by astronomer Tycho Brahe (1546–1601) in 1572 and German-born astronomer and mathematician Johannes Kepler (1571–1630) in 1604. Prior to these discoveries, Chinese and other observers recorded the appearance of a 'guest star' in 1054 in the constellation of Taurus. The star was reported to have exceeded the brightness of Venus in the night sky despite being 5,870 light-years away. The debris from these ancient supernovae explosions is still clearly observable today. For example, the Crab Nebula in the constellation of Taurus is the remnant of the supernova of 1054. The expelled envelope of the massive star that died is expanding into space at many thousands of kilometres per second. The powerful shock wave from the blast heats and compresses the ejected material, raising temperatures to a few million degrees Celsius, thus generating not only radiation in the visible waveband, but also ultraviolet and X-rays.

Another example of supernova debris is the Vela remnant, which resulted from a massive star that exploded about 11,000 years ago at a relatively nearby distance of 815 light-years. This makes Vela one of the closest supernova remnants to Earth. It is predicted that at the time of detonation, this supernova would have briefly outshone the Moon. The stellar debris is now spread over great distances, forming a complex pattern of filaments and shells. The full extent of the Vela remnant spans about eight degrees of angle in the sky, which is 16 times that subtended by the Full Moon. The study of supernova remnants is important for understanding not only how our Galaxy evolves, but also the way gas in the interstellar medium is heated up, and the manner in which various chemical elements are distributed through space.

RIGHT: *Combined optical and X-ray image of a bright supernova remnant called N9 in our neighbouring galaxy, the Large Magellanic Cloud.*

OVERLEAF LEFT: *Detailed mosaic image of the Crab nebula, which is the remnant of a supernova explosion that was first recorded by astronomers almost 1,000 years ago.*

OVERLEAF RIGHT: *Wispy hot gas seen in a small region of the Pencil Nebula, which is part of the very extended Vela supernova remnant.*

The Supernova of 1987

The supernova most extensively studied to date exploded on 23 February 1987, in the Large Magellanic Cloud, which is the small neighbouring galaxy to our own, about 170,000 light-years from Earth. Designated SN1987A, it was bright enough to be in seen in the Southern Hemisphere with the naked-eye. The supernova became the immediate target of numerous telescopes and space observatories, which were employed to record the early evolution of this tremendous event. The massive star that detonated was a blue B3-type supergiant, which had fortunately been observed prior to the explosion as part of other studies of stars in the Large Magellanic Cloud.

The progenitor star was probably born with a mass of about 20 times that of the Sun. It had already shed several Sun masses equivalent of material in the form of winds and shells during its rapid evolution in the lead up to the supernova. At its peak, the luminous power of the SN1987A explosion was almost 100 million times that of the Sun. Shock waves from the supernova generated tremendous heat energy, causing the star's ejected outer layers to glow brightly for the first 20 days or so after the event. Following this period, additional energy was provided by the decay of radioisotopes that formed during the explosion, including cobalt and nickel.

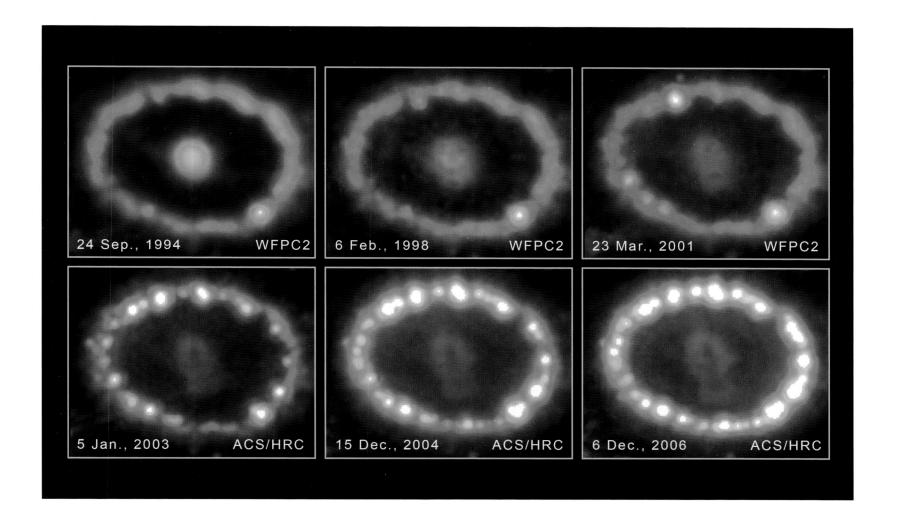

24 Sep., 1994 — WFPC2

6 Feb., 1998 — WFPC2

23 Mar., 2001 — WFPC2

5 Jan., 2003 — ACS/HRC

15 Dec., 2004 — ACS/HRC

6 Dec., 2006 — ACS/HRC

LEFT: *A composite of several Hubble Telescope images of supernova SN1987A, surrounded by its inner and outer rings and vast star-forming clouds of gas and dust in the Large Magellanic Cloud.*

ABOVE: *Hubble Space Telescope images spanning more than 12 years reveal changes in rings of material previously shed by the star that exploded as SN1987A.*

The SN1987A explosion heralded the start of a new discipline called neutrino astronomy. The theory of supernovae predicts that a tremendous amount of energy would be carried away in the form of fast-moving neutrinos that are created as the cores of the massive stars collapse. On 23 February 1987, the Kamiokande II underground detector, also used in the detection of neutrinos from the Sun, recorded nine neutrinos in a two-second interval, followed by three more detections about ten seconds later. A similar detection was also made on the same day by the IMB neutrino detector, located in Ohio in the United States.

Though huge quantities of neutrinos were produced by SN1987A, they interact so very infrequently that billions of them would have passed through Earth and remained undetected. The few that were detected were thus very significant, providing direct experimental confirmation of the theory of how massive stars explode and the physics of the way the stellar core collapses.

The Hubble Space Telescope was launched about three years after SN1987A first appeared, and it has since been monitoring the aftermath of the explosion. The initial surprise was the revelation of three glowing rings around

SN1987A. The rings are expanding up to 2,000 times slower than the supernova shock wave had, and are thought to be the relics of previous stages in the evolution of the massive star before it detonated. A pair of outer rings was formed as stellar winds from the progenitor B3-type star swept up gas ejected during earlier phases of the star's life. A 1.3 light-year diameter inner ring, rich in elements such as nitrogen, is also present, and is likely an expulsion from when the star was at its red supergiant phase, about 20,000 years ago.

Over time, the faster material ejected from the supernova explosion will crash into these slower propagating rings and overtake them. Indeed, the latest images from the Hubble Space Telescope have revealed that this collision is already starting to occur. Dozens of bright spots have appeared in the inner ring as the blast wave rams into it, causing knots of matter to heat up and glow. The high-definition imagery is also beginning to reveal the innermost debris from the supernova, which will ultimately spread out to form a hot, turbulent remnant. SN1987A has beyond a doubt provided us with a fascinating opportunity to witness in detail the death of a massive star.

Supernova Cosmology

The spectacular and explosive demise of a single massive star such as SN1987A is classified as a Type II supernova. A partially similar event can also occur in a binary star system, where material is being gravitationally pulled from a giant star and dumped onto the surface of a compact white dwarf star. An isolated white dwarf star would remain stable from any further structural changes provided its mass never exceeds about 1.4 times that of the Sun. This maximum mass limit is known as the Chandrasekhar limit, after the stellar theories worked out by the astrophysicist Subrahmanyan Chandrasekhar. In the binary star case, however, the swollen red giant star transfers additional matter onto the white dwarf via a spinning disk of hot gas.

The excess material causes the white dwarf's inner pressure and temperature to rise, causing the inert compact star to come to life again through the onset of a new phase of nuclear reactions. As the temperature rises further, the reactions proceed at an ever-increasing rate, rapidly leading to a nuclear flash that blows apart the white dwarf star. This explosion within a binary star is known as a Type 1a supernova.

Type 1a supernovae are significant events that can be detected in distant galaxies since they are extraordinarily luminous. They can therefore be studied to provide one of the most reliable measurements of distances on scales of almost three billion light-years. This makes Type 1a supernovae very important in the study of cosmology, and also in understanding the evolution of the Universe. The

RIGHT: *The supernova of a massive star is highlighted* (top right) *in the outer regions of the galaxy NGC 2403, which is located 11 million light-years from Earth.*

stellar explosions can outshine a normal galaxy for many days. Several of these types of supernovae can be detected per year in massive groupings of galaxies, such as the Virgo cluster.

In recent years, teams of astronomers have been hunting and analysing the properties of Type 1a supernovae to record their distances, using the data to measure the rate at which the Universe is expanding. The results from these studies have caused headline-making upheavals in cosmology and physics. Originally, scientists had expected to use the Type 1a supernovae in far-off galaxies to determine the rate at which the expansion of the Universe was slowing down, long after its Big Bang origin about 14 billion years ago. The astonishing new result was that the very distant Type 1a supernovae were fainter than predicted. This implies that the hosting galaxies are moving away at a greater and greater rate. Instead of slowing down as expected, the expansion of the Universe therefore appears to be accelerating in time.

These supernova observations have raised new and exciting challenges in our search for an explanation as to why we live in an accelerating Universe. A currently popular suggestion is that the unexpected increase in the expansion rate of the Universe is due to a force that acts against gravity so as to cause the acceleration. This enigmatic force has been given the name 'dark energy', which some scientists believe accounts for almost 75 per cent of the total mass of the Universe. We are, however, only at the infancy of understanding the nature of dark energy, and it has yet to be directly observed in the laboratory or the Universe.

ABOVE: *A cluster of massive galaxies called Abell 1689 is acting like a vast lens to bend the light from galaxies located at great distances behind it.*

The Biggest Explosions Since the Big Bang

Following serendipitous discoveries by US military satellites in the 1960s, orbiting observatories of the 1990s such as the Compton Gamma Ray Observatory and the Burst and Transient Source Experiment have recorded some of the most powerful explosions in the known Universe since the Big Bang.

Enigmatic gamma-ray bursts have been detected over the entire celestial sphere. These intense flashes of gamma radiation are located in distant galaxies, and each is equivalent to almost ten ordinary supernova explosions. The bursts can last between one hundredth of a second to several minutes.

One explanation for the origin of these phenomenally energetic events is that they are linked to the destruction of the most massive stars in the Universe. Known as hypernovae, they represent scaled-up versions of supernova explosions, and are thought to mark the demise of stars born with an initial mass of 30 Sun masses or more.

An example of a bright gamma ray burst was detected on 29 March 2003, by NASA's High Energy Transient Explorer satellite, in the direction of the constellation Leo. Within 90 minutes, the afterglow of the gamma-ray explosion was detected at optical wavebands by telescopes on Earth. Detailed spectrograms were then recorded by eight-metre-class telescopes of the European Southern Observatory in Chile, which revealed that the powerful event occurred in a galaxy 2,650 million light-years away. The spectra also provided evidence for the emergence of hypernova ejecta travelling out at speeds of more than 30,000 kilometres per second (18,600 miles per second). The fact that the material was expelled at almost 10 per cent of the speed of light is a testament to the incredible power of the explosion, which was likely the demise of a star 25 times more massive than the Sun.

The mechanism by which the intense gamma radiation is produced is still under debate. One possibility is that it is squirted in jets of matter that emerge from the magnetic poles of the massive star, which then slam into surrounding material that has been previously ejected. An alternative scenario is that as a massive rapidly spinning star collapses, its core is squeezed to form a black hole. The rest of the star is then consumed into the black hole via a hot, spinning disk of matter that radiates energetic gamma rays.

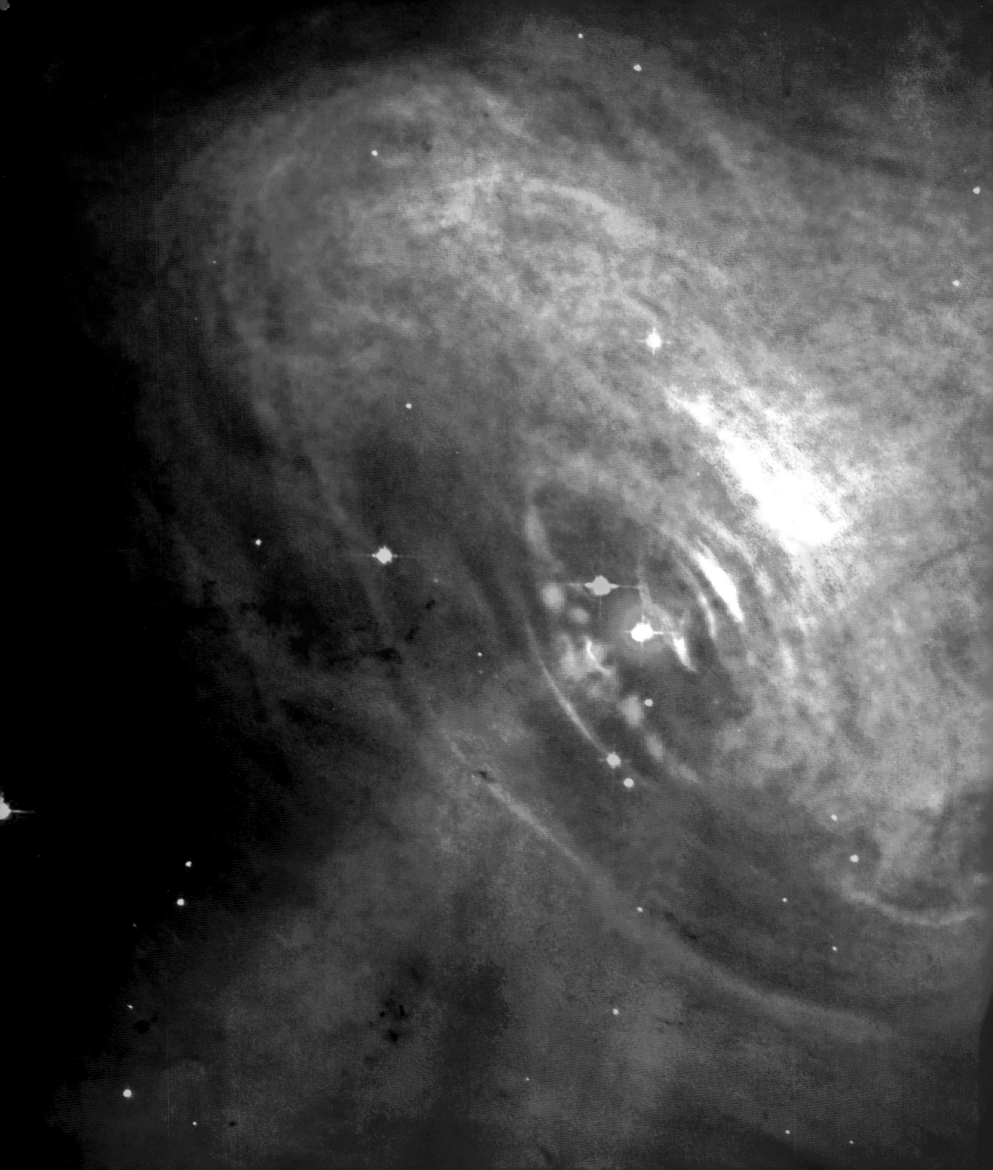

Exotic Stellar Tombstones

We saw in the previous chapter that stars evolve through a variety of stages during their lives, and that their ultimate demise is acted out in extreme and highly energetic conditions. The remnant objects at the end-points of stellar evolution are directly related to how massive the star was at birth. When low-mass stars like the Sun, intermediate-mass stars and very massive stars die, they leave strange bodies behind, known respectively as white dwarfs, neutron stars and black holes. These three stellar tombstones are among the most exotic and enigmatic objects in the Universe, and they push our imaginations to the limit and represent some of the most intriguing states of matter. As end-states in the life span of stars, these three objects provide unique laboratories for testing the extreme predictions of the theories of physics, from general relativity to quantum mechanics.

LEFT: *Composite X-ray and optical image of the highly energetic and active inner region around the Crab Nebula pulsar.*

White Dwarfs

White dwarf stars mark the burnt-out and collapsed final states of all Sun-like stars. They are remnants of stars that shined through the energy generated from nuclear fusion in their cores, but they are not massive enough to explode as Type II supernovae. The white dwarf left behind by the Sun will be mostly made of carbon, since that is the product of the final helium nuclear fusion stage that occurs for most low-mass stars. Though the surface temperature of these crushed stars can range between 4,700 degrees Celsius (9,000 degrees Fahrenheit) to more than 180,000 degrees Celsius (320,000 degrees Fahrenheit), they are intrinsically very faint because they have a very small radius. The Sun as a white dwarf will have been squeezed down to about the size of the Earth. This remarkable packing under gravity means that the white dwarf is almost 200,000 times denser than the Earth. To illustrate the point, if you could bring a teaspoon of white dwarf material to the Earth, it would weigh five tons.

White dwarf stars are difficult to find because they are so dim. Ironically, the first example to be discovered was actually a companion star to Sirius, the brightest star visible in the night sky. The star, known as Sirius B, was first directly observed in 1862, and its precise nature has challenged astronomers ever since. By studying the manner in which the two stars orbit around each other, the mass of Sirius B has been estimated to be 98 per cent of that of the Sun, yet its brightness and temperature indicate that it has a diameter smaller than that of the Earth. These parameters mean that Sirius B is very dense, with an intense gravitational pull that is 300,000 times greater than that which we experience on the Earth's surface. This density is consistent with the compact object being a carbon white dwarf star.

A happy hunting ground for uncovering white dwarf stars is a globular cluster, which, as we noted earlier, is a very dense collection of ancient stars. Globular clusters, which formed early on in the history of the Milky Way Galaxy, provide important information about the age of the Universe. One of the nearest globular clusters to Earth is called M4, located about 7,000 light-years away toward the constellation of Scorpius. M4 is estimated to be about 14 billion years old, which means it is packed with numerous highly evolved stars that are at the end of their lives. Hubble Space Telescope images of M4 have revealed 75 white dwarf stars in just one small patch of the cluster, and it is anticipated that there are tens of thousands more hidden away from our view. The light detected from these extremely faint stellar corpses in M4 is less than that of a 100-watt bulb placed on the Moon and viewed from Earth.

Another globular cluster probed in detail by the Hubble Space Telescope is NGC6395, which is 8,200 light-years away in the constellation of Ara. The cluster is extremely densely packed with an incredible number of stars, some of which are even colliding together to form new, bright young stars. In other cases, the tight packing creates binary star systems; a unique example is the system created when a normal star is paired in a very close orbit with a white dwarf star. These binary systems are called cataclysmic variables, in which matter is transferred from the normal star onto the white dwarf through a swirling disk. The inner regions of this disk, close to the white dwarf, can get very hot and can generate large amounts of ultraviolet radiation.

The incredibly high density inside a white dwarf arises because there are no nuclear energy sources left to heat

ABOVE: *Up to 13-billion-year-old white dwarf stars are revealed in the globular cluster M4.*

RIGHT: *Ancient white dwarf stars located in our Milky Way Galaxy, about 5,600 light-years from Earth.*

the gas and provide the pressure to withstand the strong self-gravity of the star. The effect is thus to condense the star into a volume equal to about that of the Earth. What, then, provides the force to keep that star from collapsing toward total destruction? An outward pressure provided by tightly squeezed electrons eventually halts the contraction of the star.

The extreme conditions inside a white dwarf were only understood following the development in the 1920s of the quantum theory of matter. Quantum mechanics is the study of how atomic particles such as electrons, protons and neutrons behave. One of the rules of quantum mechanics is that two electrons located in the same place cannot have identical velocities. In the interior of a dense white dwarf, the electrons are so closely packed that some are forced to have higher velocities, or higher energy states. The electrons are forced to have higher velocities not because they are hotter, but rather because there is nowhere else for them to go. This circumstance creates a new kind of pressure called 'electron degeneracy pressure', which then provides the force to stop the gravitational collapse of the white dwarf star.

During the 1930s, the Nobel Prize-winning astrophysicist Subrahmanyan Chandrasekhar discovered that electron degeneracy pressure can only work to support a star provided the white dwarf mass remained below a limit of about 1.4 times the mass of the Sun. If the mass left over after a star's life is greater than this 'Chandrasekhar limit', the collapse of the remnant core would continue beyond that of a white dwarf. Electrons cannot provide the much greater pressure needed to support the core, since the rules of quantum mechanics would require them to exceed the speed of light. For stars whose remnant corpses are greater than 1.4 times the mass of the Sun, the gravitational collapse continues onward to form the next exotic tombstone: the neutron star.

RIGHT: *The Illustration compares the relative sizes of the white dwarf star Sirius B and the Earth.*

Neutron Stars

Neutron stars are the exotic collapsed cores that are left behind at the end of the life of a massive star. We saw in *The Evolution and Demise of Stars* (*see page 139*) that stars born with a mass of between 8 and 25 times the mass of the Sun evolve relatively quickly through red supergiant phases, and detonate as supernovae explosions. The remnant stellar object after this destruction is a highly compressed neutron star. Though more than a thousand of these bizarre tombstones are known today, they were originally confirmed to exist in the Universe only about 40 years ago.

In 1932, physicist James Chadwick (1891–1974) discovered the neutron, a sub-atomic particle with no electric charge and a mass about the same as the positively charged proton. Following almost immediately on from this discovery, astronomers started to ponder whether, in the very extreme conditions in the core of a star, it might be possible for electrons and protons to combine to form neutrons. Astrophysicists Franz Zwicky (1898–1974), Walter Baade (1893–1960) and Robert Oppenheimer (1904–1967) later predicted that the remnants left over after supernovae explosions might indeed be held under such extreme pressures, such that the compressed cores transform into balls of neutrons. To achieve densities equivalent to that in the nucleus of an atom, a typical neutron star would have to be tiny, with a likely radius of just 10 kilometres (6 miles). Besides accepting that matter could ever be held in such incredible conditions, a major problem for astronomers was how they could possibly detect such a tiny, dim object.

Proof of the existence of neutron stars came serendipitously in 1967, when astronomers Jocelyn Bell (b.1943) and Antony Hewish (b.1924) were using a radio telescope in Cambridge to study astronomical objects that emitted fluctuating radio signals. They discovered a peculiar signal of regular radio pulses toward the constellation of Cygnus. The radio waves detected from this source were varying every 1.3373 seconds, in a clockwork manner; no astronomical source known at the time emitted radio flashes in such a precisely regulated manner. Shortly after this discovery, new pulsating radio sources, subsequently named pulsars, were detected in other directions of the sky, which immediately ruled out extra-terrestrial civilizations as potential sources for the enigmatic signals. The short radio pulses had to be coming from a rotating beam emitted by a star, somewhat like the way a beam of light from a lighthouse is seen as regular flashes when viewed from a distance. The problem was that since the time between pulses was so short – sometimes down to less than a second – the star would have to be very small to enable it to spin fast enough. Even an Earth-sized white dwarf star was deemed too big to account for such rapid radio flashes.

The mystery of the pulsars was solved toward the end of 1968, when observations of the Crab supernova remnant and the Vela nebula both revealed pulsars at their centres. Astronomers concluded that pulsars are in fact neutron stars left behind after the supernova explosions: just as an ice skater increases her rotational speed by drawing in her arms to become smaller, so the rotation of a neutron star increases rapidly as it shrinks during formation. The compression also squeezes together the magnetic field lines that run through the neutron star, leaving it with a considerably stronger magnetic field. The pulses of radio radiation detected by the radio telescopes are then beamed along the tightly bundled magnetic field lines of the star.

Just as the Earth's magnetic pole is off-set toward northern Canada from the planet's true rotation or geographic pole, a similar off-set occurs in neutron stars. This misalignment of the poles creates the 'Lighthouse effect', such that each time the rapidly spinning beam from a neutron star flashes across the Earth, we detect a pulse of radio waves.

A typical neutron star has a mass of between one-and-a-half and two times the Sun, is squeezed into a radius of 10 kilometres (6 miles), and spins up to a thousand times per second. The density of a neutron star can exceed that of the already compact white dwarf by a billion times: if one could bring a spoonful of neutron star material to Earth, it would weigh as much as a large mountain.

Being a solid object, one could imagine standing on the surface of a neutron star, but such a 'visit' would be extremely brief; its intense gravity would mean that an average adult human would now weigh a billion tons, crushing his or her body so as to become thinner than a sheet of paper. The effect of such enormously strong gravity means that the smoothest surfaces in the Universe are found on neutron stars. Unsurprisingly, the amazing properties of neutron stars attract scientists who are eager

ABOVE: *The giant Lovell radio telescope in the United Kingdom has successfully revealed the properties of pulsars.*

RIGHT: *Chandra X-ray observation of a supernova remnant which hosts a central, rapidly spinning, neutron star.*

to push to extremes the theories of nuclear physics, gravity and magnetic fields.

An isolated neutron star will slowly radiate its heat energy and cool over billions of years to reach the same frigid temperature as the cold Universe around it. As the star rotates and radiates it also loses its momentum to spin, and will gradually slow down. The spin of the pulsing neutron star at the centre of the Crab supernova remnant is, for example, slowing down at a rate of 100 millionths of a second per day. The dead star will eventually stop rotating, cool down and become an inert, undetectable object.

Since the late 1970s, Earth-orbiting telescopes have detected repeating pulses of X-ray and gamma ray radiation arriving from various directions in the sky. The energy released in some of these individual bursts is phenomenal, and can amount to that radiated by the Sun in 3,000 years.

The origin of these repeating high-energy flashes is thought to relate to a special class of neutron stars known as magnetars. Magnetars are unique in that they have the most powerful magnetic fields in the Universe. When these fossil stars are created after a supernova explosion of a massive star, they are not only highly compressed – they also spin much faster than an ordinary neutron star. If the compacted core is spinning more than 200 rotations per second, a dynamo effect is created that helps to build up a stronger field, and thus a magnetar is created.

The magnetic field of a normal neutron star is already about one billion times stronger than that of the Earth, but the field of a magnetar is a further 1,000 times more powerful than that of a neutron star. (To illustrate the point, if you placed a magnet of this strength at a distance half way between the Earth and the Moon, it would erase the data contained in the magnetic strips of all of our credit cards.) While more than 1,500 neutron stars have been discovered so far, there are less than a dozen known magnetars.

The magnetic fields of magnetars are so powerful that they very occasionally make the crust of the complicated neutron star buckle. This causes 'star quakes', which can be used to learn more about the make-up of the exotic interior of the star, somewhat like the way a geologist probes the interior of the Earth using seismic waves set up by earthquakes. The quakes on a magnetar can release a random flash of gamma rays, which can be detected using orbiting telescopes tuned to this waveband.

Neutron stars don't always occur in isolation. Some may form as part of a binary star system that has survived one of the two stars exploding as a supernova. The result can be to leave a high-mass binary system, where a normal supergiant star is paired in a close orbit with a neutron

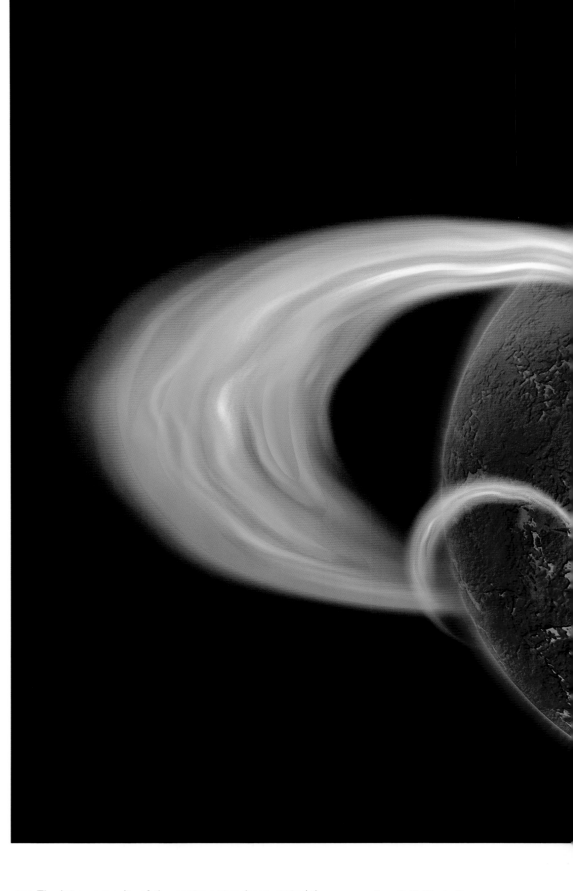

star. The intense gravity of the neutron star draws material away from the supergiant through a hot-plate-like disk of gas. As matter spirals in toward the neutron star, gas rubs against itself to generate friction that heats it to millions of degrees, thus causing it to emit X-rays.

It is possible for the evolution of an X-ray binary to proceed such that both stellar components detonate as supernovae at different times, leaving behind a close-

ABOVE: *An artist's illustration of a magnetar.*

orbiting pair of neutron stars. Double-neutron star systems are the expected evolution end-points of two massive stars that have been orbiting each other, perhaps from the time of birth, among a cluster of stars. As the pair of neutron stars radiate and orbit, they start to spiral toward each other over millions or billions of years. The eventual merger of the two super-dense stars would result in a very powerful event that generates a brief burst of gamma ray radiation, and leads to the creation of a black hole. It is thought that collisions between black holes are responsible for very short gamma ray bursts detected at Earth, which usually have durations of less than one second. Space-borne observatories such as Swift and Hete-2 have been detecting 100-millisecond-long gamma ray bursts that are likely to result from highly magnetized neutron stars crashing into each other.

ABOVE: *The core region of the M15 globular cluster (top) hosts a fascinating neutron star binary (bottom).*

Black Holes: Gravity's Ultimate Triumph

The atoms within a neutron star are completely crushed; so tight is the packing that protons capture clouds of electrons and become neutrons. Similar to the way electrons provide the pressure to withstand gravity in a white dwarf star, it is now the neutrons that offer the resisting force, in what is the last stand against gravity. When neutrons are brought together under remarkably compact conditions, they produce enormous pressures that act to halt any further gravitational collapse, thus making a stable neutron star. However, if the amount of material left behind after a supernova explosion is greater than about three times the mass of the Sun, gravity will win the ultimate battle against a star. The degeneracy pressure from neutrons is no longer sufficient, and there is no known force to prevent a complete collapse of the stellar corpse. The star compresses toward the point of infinite density and zero volume, which creates a singularity, or single point (as it is known in mathematics). The gravitational pull in the close vicinity of this object is so great that nothing, not even light, can escape from it. For this reason, the strangest of all of the end products of stellar evolution is known as a 'black hole'.

To understand black holes it is necessary to call upon Einstein's theory of general relativity and the notion of 'escape velocity'. For a rocket to overcome the pull of the Earth's gravity, it needs to be propelled to a velocity of more than 11 kilometres per second (6.8 miles per second). Known as the escape velocity, this depends on the mass and size of the planet. For example, to escape from the surface of a 10-kilometre (6-mile) radius neutron star of about the Sun's mass, a body would need to reach a velocity of 250,000 kilometres per second (155,000 miles per second).

In the late 18th century, French mathematician and astronomer Pierre-Simon Laplace proposed the notion that if a massive object were made sufficiently dense, the escape velocity on its surface would exceed that of the speed of light. Furthermore, according to Einstein's theory of special relativity, nothing within the Universe can travel faster than the speed of light, which is 300,000 kilometres per second (186,400 miles per second).

Since the photons of light do not have mass, they are not affected by a gravitational pull in the same way as ordinary matter. So the question becomes: how are photons trapped within a black hole? In 1915, Albert Einstein incorporated gravity into the concept of his theory of special relativity to propose a new theory of general relativity. A fundamental prediction of this theory is that all matter warps and bends space in its proximity. Thus, the Sun causes a curvature of space-time around it, and this curvature determines the curved orbits followed by the planets. To illustrate this, imagine the way a large, stretched-out sheet of rubber will sag when a heavy object is placed on it. In this analogy, if marbles were rolled along the sheet, those that are directed near the heavy object will have their paths distorted and deflected. At the same time, those marbles that are rolled very far away from the object will be well clear of the bends in the rubber sheet, and thus their paths will not be deflected at all. In a similar way, the path of light is bent as it travels through a curvature in space-time. In the vicinity of a black hole, the curvature of space is so extreme that it folds over on itself. Photons of light become entirely trapped in orbits that cannot escape from the black hole. The interior of a black hole is thus effectively cut-off from the rest of the Universe.

Contrary to what some might imagine, black holes are not monstrous vacuum cleaners that suck in everything around them. The journey of no return into a black hole only starts when objects approach within a certain close distance to the black hole, known as the event horizon, or the Schwarzschild radius. Beyond this critical point, there is no danger of being 'sucked in'. For instance, if the Sun was suddenly replaced by a black hole of the same mass, its event horizon would be at a radius of only 3 kilometres (1.9 miles) from the black hole. Only objects that came within this narrow boundary would be gravitationally trapped. Thus, the orbits of the Earth and all other planets would not be affected at all. As a rule, the greater the mass of a black hole, the larger the radius of its event horizon. Matter would have to approach within 15 kilometres (9.3 miles) to be trapped by a black hole that is five times the mass of the Sun, while an Earth-mass black hole would have an event horizon about the size of a grape.

Since light cannot escape from a black hole, we cannot simply point a telescope and detect one. Black holes are uncovered indirectly, by their unique influence on surrounding matter. A common example occurs when a black hole is part of a binary star system with a normal star, and matter is being drawn away from the latter on to the black hole. As the material is pulled, it forms a spiralling hot disk, which gains kinetic energy and heats up under the increasing gravitational force. At temperatures of a few million degrees, the atoms of gas emit strong X-rays, which are radiated in space before the matter crosses the event horizon. It is then that the strength and properties of the X-rays can be measured to infer the presence of a black hole.

RIGHT: *X-ray image of hot gas arising from the exotic central regions of our Milky Way Galaxy.*

ABOVE: *Illustration of a 16 Sun-mass black hole pulling matter from a massive star. X-rays emitted from this system have been detected (inset).*

RIGHT: *Hubble Space Telescope view toward the core of the Centaurus A galaxy, which is predicted to host a massive black hole.*

infrared, ultraviolet and X-ray wavebands have revealed that stars close to the centres of many galaxies, including our Milky Way Galaxy, are moving very fast and orbiting an unseen massive object. The radiation seen from the centres of these galaxies fluctuates relatively quickly in time, which suggests that the central 'engine' powering this action is likely to be very compact. The only explanation is that super-massive black holes reside in the centres of such galaxies.

The 10-metre-diameter (0.006-mile-diameter) Keck telescopes in Hawaii and the NTT telescopes in Chile have tracked the orbits of stars around the centre of our Galaxy for over ten years. The stars are orbiting at speeds of millions of kilometres per hour. Astronomers have used precise measurements of this orbital behaviour to calculate that the central object pulling these stars around so rapidly must have a mass of almost three million times that of the Sun. This huge mass must be compressed into a dimension of less than one light-year, which means that a super-massive black hole seems to be present at the centre of our Galaxy. The event horizon of this black hole would be about 50 times the Earth-to-Sun distance, a very small span compared to the overall size of the galaxy.

There are many unanswered questions concerning the precise nature of black holes; no one really knows what exists within their event horizons. The extreme states of matter in black holes will ultimately require an understanding of how gravity acts on the smallest of scales. This is a complex area of physics, where quantum mechanics meets gravity and involves the current frontier subject of quantum gravity. Meanwhile, we are left with many speculative and fictional notions, such as 'worm holes' connecting two copies of a black hole, thus permitting rapid travel across the Universe.

Another hypothetical example is the existence of 'white holes', which are sometimes mooted as the opposite of black holes, where gravity repels rather than attracts matter. Yet another scenario is that of black holes leading to other, parallel, Universes that are separate from ours. None of these bizarre phenomena have ever been observed, and there is no experimental evidence for them. We do know, however, that provided the theory of general relativity gives us the correct description of gravity, black holes stand as one of its fundamental predictions.

We saw in *The Stellar Zoo* (*see page 89*) individual cases of X-ray binaries where the X-rays detected from the system provide information on the gravitational force needed to make the matter ripped off the ordinary star so hot (Cygnus X-1, for example). In fact, the forces required can only be provided by compact objects with masses that exceed the maximum mass limit for a neutron star, and a black hole is thus the most likely candidate. Black holes with masses more than 20 times that of the Sun have been uncovered in X-ray binary systems.

We have considered so far the creation of black holes through the evolution of stars that are tens of times more massive than the Sun. It is also believed that there are other ways of making black holes in the Universe. One possibility is that during the formation of galaxies, or as a result of collisions between galaxies, gas collected at the centre may become so incredibly compressed and dense that it could create a black hole that is perhaps millions of times the mass of the Sun. Indeed, observations made in radio,

apparent brightness - the observed brightness of an astronomical object as measured by an observer on Earth.

asteroid - a small rocky body in space. Several thousand asteroids in the Solar System reside in the "belt" that lies between the orbits of Mars and Jupiter. Sometimes called a minor planet.

atom - the building blocks of matter, each element (such as hydrogen or iron) is characterized by a unique type of atom.

aurora - a light display that results when charged particles from the Solar wind enter the Earth's atmosphere around the north or south poles. Sometimes called Northern or Southern Lights.

Big Bang theory - a theory of cosmology to describe the expansion of the Universe, which is presumed to have begun with an explosive event about 14 billion years ago.

binary star - two stars that are gravitationally bound together and orbit one another. Many stars are found to be in binary-star systems.

black hole - an object or region of space with such strong gravitational pull that nothing (not even light) can escape from it.

brown dwarf - more massive than planets but not massive enough to undergo nuclear fusion of hydrogen in its core and become a star; brown dwarfs are "failed stars".

celestial - relating to the sky.

celestial sphere - an imaginary globe surrounding the Earth, to mark the apparent positions in the sky of astronomical objects, such as planets and stars.

centre of mass - the average position of a collection of massive bodies, weighted according to their distances from the centre of mass.

cepheid variable - a particular class of luminous pulsating stars with associated cyclic changes in brightness. The period of repetition is related to the true luminosity of the star, making these variable stars useful for measuring astronomical distances.

charge-coupled device (CCD) - an electronic device used to detect electromagnetic radiation at the focus of a telescope (or camera lens).

chromosphere - the lower atmosphere of the Sun, lying between the photosphere and the corona.

cluster of galaxies - a collection of galaxies that are gravitationally bound together. A cluster may contain several thousand galaxies.

comet - a small body made mostly of dust and ice, in an elliptical orbit about the Sun. As a comet nears the Sun, some of its material boils off to form a long tail.

constellation - grouping of stars identified on the celestial sphere. Many constellations are named after characters or beasts from ancient mythology.

core - referring to the central part of an object, such as planet, star or galaxy.

corona (of the Sun) - the tenuous and extremely hot outer atmosphere of the Sun.

cosmology - study of the origin and evolution of the Universe as a whole.

crust - the outer surface layer of a terrestrial planet or solid body.

dark energy - enigmatic force or energy postulated to explain the acceleration of the expansion of the Universe.

dark matter - an enigmatic component of the Universe with the attributes of mass and therefore gravity, but giving off no light that can be detected at any part of the electromagnetic spectrum.

density - the amount of mass contained in a certain volume.

disk - a flattened rotating structure of gas and possibly dust.

Doppler effect - the change in colour of light when the source of the light and the instrument of observation are moving with respect to one another. An analogous effect with sound is when changes are noted in the pitch of a whistle as a train passes by.

eclipse - an event during which one object passes in front of another.

electromagnetic radiation - another term for light. The radiation consists of waves moving through the build up of electric and magnetic fields.

electromagnetic spectrum - the complete range of light as characterized by wavelength, frequency, or energy. Examples include X-ray light, ultraviolet light, visible light, infrared light, and radio waves.

electron - a negatively charged sub-atomic particle that normally moves about the nucleus of an atom.

element - a substance that cannot be reduced by chemical processes into a simpler substance.

elliptical galaxy - a type of galaxy that appears oval shaped on the sky.

equator - a circle on the surface of a sphere, 90 degrees from each pole.

event horizon - the distance from which light can just escape from a black hole. Any closer and the light will be trapped in the black hole.

extra-galactic - anything beyond our Milky Way Galaxy.

extrasolar planet (exoplanet) - a planet orbiting around another star other than the Sun.

flare - an explosive event occurring in or near an active region on the Sun.

force - action on an object that causes its momentum to change.

fusion (nuclear) - the process by which light atomic nuclei are combined into heavier ones, with a release of energy.

galaxy - collections of millions and billions of gravitationally bound stars, plus gas and dust.

Galaxy - the galaxy to which the Sun belongs. Same as the Milky Way Galaxy.

gamma rays - the most energetic form of electromagnetic radiation.

general relativity (theory of) - a theory developed by Albert Einstein in the early 1900s to relate gravity, acceleration and the structure of space.

giant (star) - an evolved phase of a star's life when the core of a star has exhausted its supply of hydrogen for nuclear fusion. As a result, the star may swell to between 10 and 100 times the size of the Sun.

globular cluster - a collection of many thousands, and sometimes millions, of stars that are gravitationally bound and located in the halos of galaxies.

gravity - the mutual attraction between objects with mass. The greater the mass of a body, the stronger its gravitational pull.

gravitational lens - a chance alignment of objects in space which results in the gravitational deflection of light rays.

greenhouse effect - the trapping by the atmosphere of some of the heat emitted by the surface of a planet, leading to an increase of the surface temperature.

halo (of galaxy) - the outer-most regions of a galaxy, containing a roughly spherical, sparse distribution of isolated stars and globular clusters.

heavy elements - in astronomy, any element other than hydrogen or helium.

helio - prefix referring to the Sun.

hypernova - the most powerful explosion known in the Universe since the Big Bang. Hypernovae emit 100 times more energy than supernovae explosions, and mark the deaths of the most massive stars.

hypothesis - an idea or concept that is put forward, but remains to be tested with experiment or observation.

infrared radiation - part of the electromagnetic spectrum just beyond the red-end of the visible range that can be seen by the eye.

interstellar medium - gas and dust intermixed in the space between stars.

irregular galaxy - a type of galaxy without obvious symmetry and not adhering to the classes of spiral or elliptical galaxies.

kinetic energy - energy associated with motion.

Kuiper belt - a region lying beyond Neptune and Pluto that is thought to contain large numbers of comets that orbit the Sun.

latitude - an angular coordinate measure for the location of objects on the Earth, either north or south of the equator.

light year - the distance travelled by light in a vacuum in one year. One light year is equal to 9,460 billion kilometres (5,880 billion miles).

Local Group - a collection of galaxies including the Milky Way Galaxy and its nearest neighbours.

luminosity - the total energy emitted by a star each second, at all wavelengths.

Magellanic Clouds - the Small and Large Magellanic Clouds are two irregular galaxies that orbit our own Galaxy. They can be seen from southern latitudes.

magnetic fields - region of space associated with a magnetised object within which magnetic forces can be detected.

magnetic poles - points on a magnetic body (such as the Earth) at which the density of magnetic lines is greatest.

magnitude - a logarithmic based system for measuring the relative brightnesses of stars. A star with a smaller numerical value of magnitude is brighter than one with a larger value.

main-sequence - a reference to stars that are undergoing nuclear fusion of hydrogen in their cores. A star spends most of its lifetime as a main-sequence star.

mass - a measure of the amount of matter contained within a body.

merger - the result of two stars or galaxies that collide.

metals - in stellar astronomy, an element other than hydrogen or helium.

microwave - short-wave radio wavelengths.

Milky Way - band of light that encircles the night sky, due to the numerous stars and nebulae lying close to the disk of our Galaxy.

model - a theoretical construct used to explain an observation or experiment.

molecule - a particle that results from the combination of two or more atoms tightly bound together.

momentum - measure of the state of motion of a body, defined as the product of its mass and velocity.

nebula - cloud of gas and dust in space.

neutrino - a particle that travels near the speed of light, having no charge and little mass. Neutrinos are for example produced during fusion reactions in the cores of stars, but rarely interact with ordinary matter.

neutron - a sub-atomic particle with mass similar to a proton but no charge.

neutron star - a star of extremely high density made almost entirely of neutrons.

nova - literally meaning "new star", a nova refers to a star (usually a white dwarf) that greatly brightens for a time as a result of an explosive event.

nuclear - referring to the nucleus of an atom.

nucleus (of atom) - the heavy central part of an atom consisting of protons and neutrons, which is orbited by one or more electrons.

nucleus (of galaxy) - the central region of a galaxy.

Oort cloud - at a distance of about a thousand billion kilometres from the Sun, the Oort Cloud is a vast reservoir of comets.

open cluster - a collection of typically hundreds or thousands of stars that are gravitationally bound together and located in the disc of the Galaxy. Open clusters are generally young and contain newly formed stars.

optical - relating in astronomy to the visible-light band of the electromagnetic spectrum.

orbit - the path of one astronomical body about another body or point.

ozone - a layer of gas in the Earth's atmosphere at a height of about 20 to 50 kilometres (12 to 30 miles) above the surface, where incoming ultraviolet radiation from the Sun is absorbed.

photosphere - the region of the Sun's atmosphere from which visible light escapes into space.

planet - a large body (rocky or gaseous) that orbits a star, has a nearly round shape, and has cleared the neighbourhood around its orbit.

planetary nebula - the ejected outer layers of a red giant star, spread over a volume a few light years across.

plasma - a gas that is fully or partially an electrical conductor.

positron - similar to an electron but with opposite (positive) charge.

pressure - refers to how much force is spread over a given area.

prism - a glass object that splits white light into a spectrum.

proton - a sub-atomic particle with charge opposite to an electron but having a much greater mass.

proto-planet - a planet that is in the process of forming.

pulsar - a spinning neutron star with strong magnetic fields that accelerate and eject high energy particles. The ejected radiation is detected as short regular radio pulses at the Earth.

radiation - usually refers to electromagnetic radiation, such as visible light, infrared, ultraviolet and so on.

radio telescope - a telescope designed to collect and detect radiation at radio wavelengths.

red giant - a large, cool star with a high luminosity and low surface temperature.

retrograde - rotation or orbital motion in a clockwise direction when viewed from above.

satellite - any smaller body (natural or artificial) orbiting a larger body.

solar eclipse - an eclipse of the Sun by the Moon, caused by the passage of the Moon in front of the Sun. Solar eclipses can only occur at the time of a New Moon.

solar system - the system of bodies that are gravitationally bound to the Sun, such as the planets, moons, comets and asteroids.

solar wind - a stream of charged particles that escape from the Sun's atmosphere at high speeds and flow out into the solar system.

space-time - combination in four dimensions of time and the three dimension of space.

special relativity (theory of) - Albert Einstein's description mechanics and electromagnetic theory to explain how distance, time and mass are affected by the motion of an observer.

spectral line - radiation at a particular wavelength of light produced by the emission or absorption of energy by an atom.

spectrograph - an instrument attached to a telescope for recording a spectrum.

spectroscopic binary star - two stars revolving around a common centre of mass that can be identified by cyclic changes in the Doppler shift of the lines of their spectra.

spectrum - the array of colours or wavelengths apparent when light is dispersed, for example by a prism.

spiral arms - structures containing young stars and interstellar material that wind out from the central regions of some galaxies.

spiral galaxy - a type of galaxy where most of the gas and stars are in a flattened disc that displays spiral arm structures. Our Milky Way Galaxy is a spiral galaxy.

star - a massive sphere of gas that shines by generating its own power.

star cluster - a collection of stars that are gravitationally bound to one another.

stellar evolution - changes in structure and properties of a star over the course of time (usually over scales of millions to billions of years).

stellar wind - the outflow of gaseous material at high speeds from a star.

Sun - the star about which the Earth is orbiting.

sunspot - a slightly cooler temporary region on the Sun's surface that appears dark by contrast to the surrounding hotter regions.

supercluster - a collection of several clusters of galaxies that spans a large region of space, but not necessarily gravitationally bound.

supergiant - an evolved phase of stellar evolution, supergiants are massive stars that can swell up to several thousand times bigger than the Sun.

supernova - one of the brightest and most violent events in the Universe that occurs when a star explodes. A Type I supernova occurs when a white dwarf accretes matter in a binary system. A Type II supernova results from the implosion of a massive star at the end of its life.

temperature - a measure of how hot or cold an object is; a measure of the average random speeds of microscopic particles in a substance.

terrestrial planet - a planet that is predominantly composed of rocky and metal substances. Earth, Venus and Mars are terrestrial planets.

theory - a set of laws and hypotheses that have been used to explain observed phenomena.

thermonuclear energy - energy that results from encounters between particles that are given high velocities (through heating).

tidal force - differences in the force of gravity across a body that is being attracted by another larger body. The result may be the deformation of the smaller body.

ultraviolet radiation - electromagnetic radiation of the region just outside the visible range, corresponding to wavelengths slightly shorter than blue light.

Universe - the total of all space, time, matter and energy.

variable star - a star whose power output changes over time.

velocity - the rate and direction in which distance is covered over some interval of time.

visible light - see optical.

visual binary star - two stars that revolve around a common centre of mass, both of which can be seen through a telescope.

void - in astronomy, regions of space between super-clusters of galaxies that appears to lack luminous matter.

watt - a measure or unit of power output.

waveband - sections of the electromagnetic spectrum such as the infrared, radio, X-ray, and so on.

wavelength - the distance between two successive peaks or troughs of a wave.

weight - the total force on some mass due to gravitational attraction.

white dwarf - the collapsed end-state of a star that has exhausted its nuclear fuel supply, and shines from residual heat.

X-rays - high-energy electromagnetic radiation, with photons of wavelengths intermediate between those of ultraviolet radiation and gamma rays.

PICTURE CREDITS

Page 1: NASA and H. Richer (University of British Columbia)
Pages 2–3: NASA/JPL-Caltech/CfA
Pages 4–5: NASA/JPL-Caltech/S. Stolovy (Spitzer Science Center/Caltech)
Page 6: NASA, The Hubble Heritage Team and A. Riess (STScI)
Pages 8–9: ESA/A. Fujii
Page 10: K. Don, NOAO/AURA/NSF/WIYN
Page 11: NOAO/AURA/NSF/WIYN
Pages: 12–13: NASA, ESA, and The Hubble Heritage Team (STScI/AURA); acknowledgement: J. Blakeslee (Washington State University)
Page 15: Isaac Newton Group of Telescopes, La Palma
Pages 16–17: NASA and STScI
Pages 18–19: (left) courtesy of Howard McCallon, (right) NASA/IRAS
Pages 20–21: NASA/JPL-Caltech
Page 21: NASA/JPL-Caltech/E. Churchwell (University of Wisconsin-Madison)
Pages 22–23: NASA, ESA, and H. Bond (STScI)
Pages 26–27: NASA, ESA, and The Hubble Heritage Team (STScI/AURA)-ESA/Hubble Collaboration
Page 28: Hubble data: NASA, ESA, and A. Zezas (Harvard-Smithsonian Center for Astrophysics); GALEX data: NASA, JPL-Caltech, GALEX Team, J. Huchra et al. (Harvard-Smithsonian Center for Astrophysics); Spitzer data: NASA/JPL/Caltech/S. Willner (Harvard-Smithsonian Center for Astrophysics)
Page 30: NASA/JPL-Caltech/N. Flagey (IAS/SSC) & A. Noriega-Crespo (SSC/Caltech)
Page 31: NASA, ESA, STScI, J. Hester and P. Scowen (Arizona State University)
Page 32: NASA/JPL-Caltech/Harvard-Smithsonian CfA/ESA/STScI
Page 33: NASA, ESA, and The Hubble Heritage Team (STScI/AURA)
Page 34: NASA, NOAO, ESA and The Hubble Heritage Team (STScI/AURA); acknowledgement:

K. Noll (Hubble Heritage PI/STScI), C. Luginbuhl (USNO), F. Hamilton (Hubble Heritage/STScI)
Page 35: NASA/JPL-Caltech/T. Megeath (University of Toledo) & M. Robberto (STScI)
Page 36: NASA, ESA, and the Hubble Heritage Team (STScI/AURA)-ESA/Hubble Collaboration; acknowledgement: D. Gouliermis (Max Planck Institute for Astronomy, Heidelberg)
Page 37: NASA, ESA, and the Hubble Heritage Team (STScI/AURA)-ESA/Hubble Collaboration
Page 38: NASA, ESA, and the Hubble Heritage Team (STScI/AURA)-ESA/Hubble Collaboration; acknowledgement: B. Whitmore (Space Telescope Science Institute)
Pages 40–41: NASA/JPL-Caltech
Page 43: NASA/JPL-Caltech/T. Pyle (SSC)
Page 45: Wolfgang Brandner (JPL/IPAC), Eva K. Grebel (Univ. Washington), You-Hua Chu (Univ. Illinois Urbana-Champaign), and NASA
Pages 46–47: NASA, ESA, P. Kalas and J. Graham (University of California, Berkeley) and M. Clampin (NASA/GSFC)
Page 48: STScI-1995-24
Page 49: Dick Schwatrz (Univ. of Missouri-St. Louis), and NASA
Page 50: NASA/JPL-Caltech/J. Bally (Univ. of Colo.)
Page 51: NASA, John Krist (Space Telescope Science Institute), Karl Stapelfeldt (Jet Propulsion Laboratory), Jeff Hester (Arizona State University), Chris Burrows (European Space Agency/Space Telescope Science Institute)
Page 52: NASA and Jeff Hester (Arizona State University)
Page 55: NASA, ESA, and The Hubble Heritage Team (STScI/AURA), W. Keel (University of Alabama, Tuscaloosa)
Pages 56–57: NASA/JPL-Caltech/Univ. of Virginia
Pages 58–59: NASA/JPL-Caltech/L. Allen (Harvard-Smithsonian CfA) & Gould's Belt Legacy Team
Pages 60–61: NASA, ESA, A. Sarajedini (University of Florida) and G. Piotto (University of Padua [Padova]); science credit: NASA, ESA, and G. Piotto (University of Padua [Padova])
Pages 62–63: NASA, ESA and AURA/Caltech
Pages 64–65: M.F. Skrutskie (UMass; Principal

Investigator, 2MASS), J.M. Carpenter (Caltech), R. Hurt (IPAC/Caltech)
Page 67: NASA, ESA and A. Nota (STScI/ESA)
Page 68: NASA/JPL-Caltech/STScI/CXC/UofA /ESA/AURA/JHU
Page 70: NASA and The Hubble Heritage Team (STScI/AURA); acknowledgement: M. Donahue (STScI) and J. Trauger (JPL)
Page 71: NASA, H. Ford (JHU), G. Illingworth (UCSC/LO), M.Clampin (STScI), G. Hartig (STScI), the ACS Science Team, and ESA
Pages 72–73: NASA, ESA, and The Hubble Heritage Team (AURA/STScI); acknowledgement: J. Higdon (Cornell U.) and I. Jordan (STScI)
Page 75: NASA, ESA, and The Hubble Heritage Team (STScI/AURA); acknowledgement: J. Blakeslee (JHU) and R. Thompson (University of Arizona)
Pages 78–79: NASA/JPL-Caltech/S. Stolovy (SSC/Caltech)
Page 81: NASA, ESA, and the Hubble Heritage (STScI/AURA)-ESA/Hubble Collaboration; acknowledgement: J. Maíz Apellániz (Institute of Astrophysics of Andalucía, Spain)
Page 82: N. A. Sharp, NOAO/AURA/NSF/WIYN
Page 83: European Space Agency & NASA; acknowledgement: E. Olszewski (University of Arizona)
Page 85: NASA, ESA, and The Hubble Heritage Team (AURA/STScI); acknowledgement: F. Bresolin (Institute for Astronomy, U. Hawaii) and the Digitized Sky Survey
Page 86: NASA/JPL-Caltech/M. Meixner (STScI) & the SAGE Legacy Team
Pages 88–89: X-ray: NASA/CXC/SAO/M. Karovska et al.; illustration: CXC/M.Weiss
Page 90: copyright ESA; illustration by Martin Kornmesser, ESA/ECF
Page 93: NASA, ESA, and J. Maíz Apellániz (Instituto de Astrofísica de Andalucía, Spain)
Page 94: NASA, ESA, The Hubble Heritage Team, (STScI/AURA) and A. Riess (STScI)
Page 97: NASA/JPL-Caltech
Pages 98–99: Bill Livingston, NOAO/AURA/NSF/ WIYN
Page 101: Photo/Image provided courtesy of the Naval Research Laboratory
Page 102: NASA and The Hubble Heritage Team

(AURA/STScI); acknowledgement: A. Cool (SFSU)

Page 105: NOAO/AURA/NSF/WIYN

Page 106: SOHO (ESA & NASA)

Page 107: The Institute for Solar Physics

Page 109: SOHO (ESA & NASA)

Page 110: (left) SOHO/LASCO, SOHO/EIT (ESA & NASA), S. Koutchmy et al (IAS/IAP/CNRS), Williams College, (right) SOHO (ESA & NASA)

Page 111: University of Iowa/NASA Scientific Visualization Studio

Page 113: SOHO (ESA & NASA)

Page 114: NASA/ESA

Page 115: NASA/ESA

Pages 116–117: SOHO (ESA & NASA)

Pages 118–119: NASA/CXC/JPL-Caltech/CfA

Page 120: NASA/JPL-Caltech

Page 121: NASA, ESA, and G. Bacon (STScI)

Page 122: ESA 2002; illustration by Medialab

Page 124: NASA

Page 125: NASA, ESA, and A. Schaller (for STScI)

Page 126: NASA, The Hubble Heritage Team and A. Riess (STScI)

Page 128–129: NASA/JPL-Caltech/H. Knutson (Harvard-Smithsonian CfA)

Page 130: NASA, ESA, G. Schneider (Steward Observatory, Univ. of Arizona, USA), I. Song (Gemini Observ.), B. Zuckerman, E. Becklin (Univ. of California, USA), P. Lowrance (California Inst. of Technology, USA), B. Macintosh (Lawrence Livermore National Laboratory, USA), M. Bessell (Australian National Univ.), and C. Dumas and G. Chauvin (European Southern Observatory)

Page 131: IAC (Instituto de Astrofísica de Canarias)

Pages 134–135: NASA, ESA, C.R. O'Dell (Vanderbilt University), M. Meixner and P. McCullough (STScI)

Page 137: NASA and Ron Gilliland (Space Telescope Science Institute)

Page 138: NASA and The Hubble Heritage Team (AURA/STScI)

Page 140–141: Image based on data obtained as part of the INT Photometric H-Alpha Survey of the Northern Galactic Plane, prepared by Nick Wright, University College London, on behalf of the IPHAS collaboration and published in 'The shaping of planetary nebula Sh 2–188 through interaction with the interstellar medium', C.J. Wareing et al., Monthly Notices of the Royal Astonomical Society, Volume 366, p. 387, February 2006.

Page 142: G. Jacoby, NOAO/AURA/NSF/WIYN

Page 144: NASA, Donald Walter (South Carolina State University), Paul Scowen and Brian Moore (Arizona State University)

Page 146: NASA, NOAO, ESA, the Hubble Helix Nebula Team, M. Meixner (STScI), and T.A. Rector (NRAO).

Page 147: NASA, ESA, HEIC, and The Hubble Heritage Team (STScI/AURA); acknowledgement: R. Corradi (Isaac Newton Group of Telescopes, Spain) and Z. Tsvetanov (NASA)

Page 149: X-ray: NASA/CXC/RIT/J.Kastner et al.; Optical/IR: BD +30 & Hen 3: NASA/STScI/Univ. MD/J.P.Harrington; NGC 7027: NASA/STScI/Caltech/J.Westphal & W.Latter; Mz 3: NASA/STScI/Univ. Washington/B.Balick

Page 150: NASA/CXC/Penn State/L.Townsley et al.; Optical: Pal Obs. DSS

Page 153: N. Smith and NOAO/AURA/NSF/WIYN

Page 154: X-ray: NASA/CXC/GSFC/M.Corcoran et al.; Optical: NASA/STScI

Page 157: NASA/JPL-Caltech

Page 159: NASA/CXC/STScI/JPL-Caltech/UIUC/Univ. of Minn.

Page 160: NASA, ESA, J. Hester and A. Loll (Arizona State University)

Page 161: NASA and The Hubble Heritage Team (STScI/AURA); acknowledgement: W. Blair (JHU) and D. Malin (David Malin Images)

Page 162: NASA and The Hubble Heritage Team (STScI/AURA)

Page 163. Copyright: NASA, ESA, and R. Kirshner (Harvard-Smithsonian Center for Astrophysics)

Page 164: NASA, ESA, A.V. Filippenko (University of California, Berkeley), P. Challis (Harvard-Smithsonian Center for Astrophysics), et al.

Page 165: NASA, N. Benitez (JHU), T. Broadhurst (Racah Institute of Physics/The Hebrew University), H. Ford (JHU), M. Clampin (STScI), G. Hartig (STScI), G. Illingworth (UCO/Lick Observatory), the ACS Science Team and ESA

Page 167: NASA

Page 168–169: X-ray Image: NASA/CXC/ASU/J. Hester et al; Optical Image: NASA/HST/ASU/J. Hester et al.

Page 170: NOAO/AURA/NSF/WIYN

Page 171: NASA and H. Richer (University of British Columbia)

Page 173: ESA/NASA

Page 174: Ian Morison, Jodrell Bank Observatory

Page 175: X-ray: NASA/CXC/Penn State/S.Park et al.; Optical: Pal.Obs. DSS

Page 176: NASA/CXC/SAO

Page 177: (top) G. De Marchi (STScI and Univ. of Florence, Italy) and F. Paresce (STScI)/NASA, ESA; (bottom) NASA/GSFC/N.White, L.Angelini

Page 179: NASA/CXC/UCLA/MIT/M.Muno et al.

Page 180: Illustration: NASA/CXC/M.Weiss; X-ray: NASA/CXC/CfA/P.Plucinsky et al.; Optical: NASA/STScI/SDSU/J.Orosz et al.

Page 181: E.J. Schreier (STScI), and NASA

INDEX